MATHS ON TARGET

Year 5

Answers

Stephen Pearce

Elmwood Press

First published 2008 by
Elmwood Press
80 Attimore Road
Welwyn Garden City
Herts. AL8 6LP
Tel. 01707 333232

ISBN 9781 902 214 979

Typeset and illustrated by Domex e-Data Pvt. Ltd.
Printed

Maths on Target Year 5 provides a simple, manageable structure to help teachers plan and teach all the objectives set out in the yearly programme in the renewed Primary Framework for Mathematics, each lesson clearly differentiated at three levels of ability.

In the renewed Framework the mathematics curriculum has been organised into seven strands.

- Using and applying mathematics
- Counting and understanding number
- Knowing and using number facts
- Calculating
- Understanding shape
- Measuring
- Handling data

For planning purposes the curriculum is structured around five blocks of work, each block drawing on three of the strands.

The five blocks are:
- Block A – Counting, partitioning and calculating
- Block B – Securing number facts, understanding shape
- Block C – Handling data and measures
- Block D – Calculating, measuring and understanding shape
- Block E – Securing number facts, relationships and calculating

Each block is further organised into three units of work. Each unit provides two or three weeks of learning. To ensure progression throughout the year the units are best taught in the following order.

	Block A	Block B	Block C	Block D	Block E
Term 1	Unit 1	Unit 1	Unit 1	Unit 1	Unit 1
Term 2	Unit 2	Unit 2	Unit 2	Unit 2	Unit 2
Term 3	Unit 3	Unit 3	Unit 3	Unit 3	Unit 3

The structure of **Maths on Target** matches that of the renewed Framework, with fifteen units arranged in the above order. Each unit in **Maths on Target** consists of lessons based upon the learning overview for that unit in the renewed Framework, with the learning intention for each lesson expressed as an *I can* statement.

All lessons in **Maths on Target** are divided into three sections, each providing material at a different level of ability. Section A: activities based upon work previously covered, generally matching the objectives for year 4 pupils.

Section B: activities based upon the objectives for Year 5 pupils. Most children should be able to work successfully at this level.

Section C: activities providing extension material for faster workers and those needing more challenging tasks, generally matching the objectives for Year 6 pupils.

MATHS ON TARGET – YEAR 5 ANSWERS

Page 2

A

1 23, 25, 27, 29, 31, 33	**2** 56, 48, 40, 32, 24, 16
3 125, 150, 175, 200, 225, 250	**4** 73, 68, 63, 58, 53, 48
5 47, 51, 55, 59, 63, 67	**6** 83, 76, 69, 62, 55, 48
7 59, 62, 65, 68, 71, 74	**8** 56, 49, 42, 35, 28, 21
9 5, 13, 21, 29, 37, 45	**10** 120, 117, 114, 111, 108, 105
11 21, 26, 31, 36, 41, 46	**12** 48, 42, 36, 30, 24, 18
13 19, 28, 37, 46, 55, 64	**14** 110, 90, 70, 50, 30, 10
15 21, 32, 43, 54, 65, 76	

B

1 91, 93, 95 +2	**2** –9, –11, –13 –2
3 25, 75, 125 –50	**4** 28, 39, 50 –11
5 60, 56, 52 –4	**6** 375, 400, 425 +25
7 –8, –4, 0 +4	**8** –4, –10, –14, –18, –22, –26 –4
9 67, 62, 57, 52 –5	**10** 15, 12, 9, 6, 0 –3
11 55, 48, 41, 34 –7	**12** 56, 49, 42, 35, 28, 21, 14 –7
13 215, 316, 417, 518, 619, 720 +111	
14 –45, –40, –35, –30 +5	
15 46, 35, 24, 13, 2 –11	
16 –10, –15, –20, –25 –5	

C

1 101, 107, 113 +6	**2** –10, –12, –14 –2
3 0.9, 1.1, 1.3 +0.2	**4** 104, 113, 122 +9
5 5, 0, –5 –5	**6** 135, 160, 185 +25
7 –5, –7, –9 –2	**8** 1.25, 1.5, 1.75 +0.25
9 88, 77, 66 –11	**10** 0.09, 0.1, 0.11 +0.01
11 86, 94, 102 +8	**12** 2, –2, –6 –4
13 8, –2, –12 –10	**14** 17, 10, 3 –7
15 16, 4, –8 –12	**16** 81, 100, 119 +19
17 –5, –11, –17 –6	**18** 132, 153, 174 +21

Page 3

A

1 –5, –4, –3, –2, –1, 0, 1, 2	**2** 3, 2, 1, 0, –1, –2, –3
3 –12, –10, –8, –6, –4, –2, 0	**4** –14, –10, –6, –2, 2, 6, 10
5 –7, –5, –3, –1, 1, 3, 5	**6** 5, 3, 1, –1, –3, –5, –7
7 1 **8** –2 **9** 3	**10** 4 **11** 0 **12** 5
13 –3 **14** –9 **15** –6	**16** –9 **17** –10 **18** –7

B

1 –11, –9, –7, –5, –3, –1, 1	**2** –11, –8, –5, –2, 1, 4, 7
3 –6, –4, –2, 0, 2, 4, 6	**4** –14, –10, –6, –2, 2, 6, 10
5 5, 3, 1, –1, –3, –5, –7	**6** 8, 6, 4, 2, 0, –2, –4
7 –6, –3, –1, 3, 7, 9	**8** –8, –2, 0, 1, 4, 9
9 –7, –4, –1, 1, 2, 6	**10** –6, –3, –2, 0, 3, 5

C

1 A –48°C   B –32°C   C –8°C   D 6°C   E 34°C
2 (a) 14°C   (b) 24°C   (c) 42°C   (d) 54°C
3 (a) –14°C   (b) –12°C   (c) –34°C   (d) 16°C

Page 4

A

1 one thousand four hundred and thirty-one km
2 six thousand three hundred and fifty-six km
3 eight thousand one hundred and thirty-eight km
4 nine hundred and fifty-two km
5 eight thousand nine hundred and thirty-six km
6 three thousand five hundred and eight km
7 five thousand and seventeen km
8 ten thousand eight hundred and fifty-two km
9 nine hundred and twenty-eight km
10 seven thousand five hundred and seven km
11

City	Distance (km)
New York	5572
Moscow	2498
Paris	342
Los Angeles	8758
Johannesburg	9071
Bombay	7190
Rio de Janeiro	9299
Buenos Aires	11131
Calcutta	7961
Toronto	5704

Page 5

B

1

Seas	Area (sq. miles)
Pacific Ocean	64 190 000
Atlantic Ocean	33 420 000
Indian Ocean	28 350 000
Arctic Ocean	5 110 000
South China Sea	1 148 000
Caribbean Sea	1 063 000
Mediterranean Sea	966 500
Baring Sea	875 700
Gulf of Mexico	595 800
Sea of Okhotsk	589 800

2 one hundred and sixty-six million two hundred and forty thousand km^2
3 eighty-six million five hundred and sixty thousand km^2
4 seventy-three million four hundred and thirty thousand km^2
5 thirteen million two hundred and thirty thousand km^2
6 two million nine hundred and seventy-four thousand km^2
7 two million seven hundred and fifty-three thousand km^2
8 two million five hundred and three thousand km^2
9 two million two hundred and sixty-eight thousand one hundred and eighty km^2
10 one million five hundred and forty-two thousand nine hundred and eighty-five km^2
11 one million five hundred and twenty-seven thousand five hundred and seventy km^2

C

1 seven million seven thousand and ninety-one
2 nine hundred and fifty-three thousand one hundred and seventy-five
3 three million four hundred and seventy-two thousand and nine
4 two million two thousand one hundred and twenty-one
5 seventy-seven thousand four hundred
6 one million eight hundred and six thousand seven hundred and thirty-seven
7 nine million three hundred and nineteen thousand three hundred and sixty-seven
8 three hundred and two thousand seven hundred and forty-seven

9 twenty-seven thousand and sixty-three

10 two million six hundred and ninety-three thousand three hundred and eighty-three

11 three million seventy-two thousand nine hundred and twenty-two

12 five hundred and twenty-nine thousand and twenty-one

13 20 579 twenty thousand five hundred and seventy-nine

20 597 twenty thousand five hundred and ninety-seven

20 759 twenty thousand seven hundred and fifty-nine

20 795 twenty thousand seven hundred and ninety-five

20 957 twenty thousand nine hundred and fifty-seven

20 975 twenty thousand nine hundred and seventy-five

25 079 twenty-five thousand and seventy-nine

25 097 twenty-five thousand and ninety-seven

25 709 twenty-five thousand seven hundred and nine

25 790 twenty-five thousand seven hundred and ninety

25 907 twenty-five thousand nine hundred and seven

25 970 twenty-five thousand nine hundred and seventy

Page 6

A

1 300 + 60 + 9		**2** 1000 + 400 + 20 + 6	
3 2000 + 100 + 90 + 3		**4** 4000 + 500 + 30 + 7	
5 3000 + 800 + 50 + 8		**6** 600 + 70 + 2	
7 5000 + 700 + 20 + 4		**8** 2000 + 900 + 10 + 7	
9 1000 + 900 + 40 + 6		**10** 1000 + 100 + 50 + 6	
11 8000 + 500 + 30 + 8		**12** 3000 + 500 + 30 + 2	

B

1 900	**2** 5	**3** 4000	**4** 600
5 80 000	**6** 400	**7** 600 000	**8** 8000
9 3 000 000	**10** 1	**11** 90 000	**12** 800 000
13 3000	**14** 200	**15** 5 000 000	**16** 17 672
17 104 813	**18** 149 628	**19** 273 497	**20** 30 813
21 1 575 628	**22** 424 157	**23** 1173 684	**24** 12 716
25 332 176	**26** 1 818 534	**27** 6 159 019	

C

1 377 496	**2** 1 863 031	**3** 2 003 193	**4** 42 584
5 1 150 267	**6** 1 194 805	**7** 1 007 436	**8** 5 215 320
9 1 029 754	**10** 2 187 362	**11** 804 169	**12** 33 174
13 25 005	**14** 21 298	**15** 135 165	**16** 1 210 371
17 94 262			

Page 7

A

1 683, 863, 2386, 2836	**2** 1945, 5149, 5419, 5914
3 2743, 3247, 3274, 3472	**4** 1386, 1638, 1836, 1863
5 4578, 4758, 4785, 4857	**6** 300 **7** 2000
8 400 **9** 60	**10** 3000 **11** 2000
12 500 **13** 4000	**14** 600 **15** 50

B

1 3478, 3874, 4738, 4837

2 52 287, 52 783, 53 827, 53 872

3 19 162, 19 216, 19 261, 19 612

4 10 606, 10 660, 16 006, 16 060

5 14 231, 14 312, 14 321, 14 421   **6** 4000

7 7000   **8** 500 000   **9** 300   **10** 600 000

C

1 3900	**2** 19 650	**3** 25 330
4 17 800	**5** 16 710	**6** 6980

7 (a) 1000s are 7 and 8   (b) 1000s are 1 and 2

       100s are 5 and 6   100s are 3 and 4

       10s are 3 and 4   10s are 5 and 6

       Units are 1 and 2   Units are 7 and 8

    (c) 1234, 8765   (d) 4876, 5123

Page 8

A

1 300	**2** 1870	**3** 6200	**4** 7140	**5** 5930
6 580	**7** 900	**8** 1600	**9** 4000	**10** 5800
11 10 000	**12** 6200	**13** 86	**14** 9	**15** 300
16 153	**17** 70	**18** 540	**19** 60	**20** 39
21 61	**22** 4	**23** 73	**24** 100	**25** 860
26 620	**27** 70	**28** 8100	**29** 139	**30** 5800
31 24	**32** 9000			

B

1 9870	**2** 170	**3** 86 000	**4** 14	**5** 52 000
6 30	**7** 740 000	**8** 4900	**9** 134 000	**10** 280
11 147 000	**12** 650	**13** 2160	**14** 830 000	**15** 960
16 740 000	**17** 80	**18** 1 000 000	**19** 1500	**20** 30 000

C

1 39 700	**2** 4 000 000	**3** 990
4 150 000	**5** 1700	**6** 400 000
7 6100 × 100	**8** 2 000 000 ÷ 1000	**9** 25 600 × 10
10 2 400 000 ÷ 100	**11** 370 000 ÷ 10	**12** 8100 × 1000
13 £10 000	**14** 10 000 000 cm	**15** 2500g
16 140 000		

Page 9

A

1 32	**2** 28	**3** 18	**4** 36	**5** 21	**6** 27
7 56	**8** 18	**9** 81	**10** 35	**11** 48	**12** 20
13 8	**14** 2	**15** 3	**16** 7	**17** 10	**18** 5
19 9	**20** 5	**21** 8	**22** 9	**23** 6	**24** 9

B

1 7	**2** 6	**3** 8	**4** 9	**5** 7
6 8	**7** 56	**8** 30	**9** 63	**10** 54
11 48	**12** 28	**13** 560	**14** 1800	**15** 180
16 3600	**17** 2000	**18** 350	**19** 16 000	**20** 4900
21 24 000	**22** 36 000	**23** 1600	**24** 4500	**25** 80
26 60	**27** 500	**28** 700	**29** 80	**30** 900
31 50	**32** 600	**33** 300	**34** 70	**35** 90
36 800				

C

1 600	**2** 30	**3** 800	**4** 700	**5** 900	**6** 50
7 450	**8** 3000	**9** 210	**10** 5400	**11** 140	**12** 4800
13 4.2	**14** 7.2	**15** 1.2	**16** 5.6	**17** 2.7	**18** 5.4
19 3.5	**20** 2.7	**21** 3.6	**22** 2.8	**23** 6.4	**24** 2.8
25 0.5	**26** 0.9	**27** 0.6	**28** 0.8	**29** 0.7	**30** 0.9
31 0.7	**32** 0.8	**33** 0.4	**34** 0.9	**35** 1.0	**36** 0.5

Page 10

A

1 25	**2** 43	**3** 47	**4** 27	**5** 69	**6** 24
7 9	**8** 117	**9** 14	**10** 34	**11** 126	**12** 26
13 350	**14** 520	**15** 8100	**16** 1740	**17** 2700	**18** 6400
19 126	**20** 144	**21** 117	**22** 121	**23** 154	**24** 198
25 72	**26** 54	**27** 56	**28** 14	**29** 8	**30** 3
31 39	**32** 54	**33** 72	**34** 48	**35** 76	**36** 92
37 92	**38** 154	**39** 112	**40** 56	**41** 122	**42** 67
43 71	**44** 94	**45** 83	**46** 54	**47** 74	**48** 38

Page 11

B

1 293	**2** 563	**3** 665	**4** 494	**5** 551	**6** 205
7 323	**8** 418	**9** 494	**10** 378	**11** 483	**12** 441
13 309	**14** 423	**15** 218	**16** 2013	**17** 3018	**18** 514

19 136　　**20** 285　　**21** 252　　**22** 168　　**23** 224　　**24** 288
25 1800　**26** 1400　**27** 6000　**28** 28 000　**29** 1500　**30** 12 000
31 31　　**32** 52　　**33** 69　　**34** 91　　**35** 29　　**36** 49
37 90　　**38** 96　　**39** 156　**40** 16　　**41** 15　　**42** 21
43 549　**44** 396　**45** 383　**46** 1001　**47** 8012　**48** 1007

C

1 372　　**2** 602　　**3** 511　　**4** 472　　**5** 672　　**6** 774
7 319　　**8** 285　　**9** 183　　**10** 257　　**11** 394　　**12** 365
13 2.8　　**14** 3.9　　**15** 4.6　　**16** 5.8　　**17** 3.6　　**18** 2.7
19 208　**20** 450　**21** 357　**22** 9　　**23** 18　　**24** 17
25 449　**26** 663　**27** 5293　**28** 872　**29** 829　**30** 2816
31 400　**32** 70　　**33** 3　　**34** 700　**35** 8　　**36** 40
37 637　**38** 612　**39** 1089　**40** 1414　**41** 784　**42** 1485
43 437　**44** 356　**45** 258　**46** 3216　**47** 2039　**48** 4031

Page 12

A

1 248　　**2** 483　　**3** 728　　**4** 383　　**5** 855　　**6** 549
7 601　　**8** 486　　**9** 447　　**10** 785　　**11** 956　　**12** 955
13 449　**14** 593

B

1 961　　**2** 1577　　**3** 1258　　**4** 1646　　**5** 1149　　**6** 1486
7 1139　**8** 2154　　**9** 2662　　**10** 3675　　**11** 5377　　**12** 6849
13 £1531

C

1 4543　　**2** 5342　　　**3** 8561　　**4** 13 446　**5** 8482
6 11 441　**7** 10 635　　**8** 13 864　**9** 11 851　**10** 12 347
11 12 501　**12** 6932 miles　**13** £10 623

Page 13

A

1 168　　**2** 312　　**3** 227　　**4** 255　　**5** 537　　**6** 58
7 256　　**8** 316　　**9** 347　　**10** 632　　**11** 591　　**12** 327

B

1 46　　**2** 26　　**3** 46　　**4** 28　　**5** 69　　　　**6** 16
7 27　　**8** 18　　**9** 37　　**10** 24　　**11** 48 miles　**12** 37

C

1 322　　**2** 140　　**3** 437　　**4** 149　　**5** 723　　**6** 317
7 153　　**8** 139　　**9** 585　　**10** 107　　**11** 167 miles

Page 14

A

1 (a) 35, 65　　(b) 58, 142　　　(c) 177, 323　　**2** 276
3 179　　　　　**4** 46 + 63　　**5** 37 + 93　　**6** 86 + 52
7 69 + 74　　**8** 92 – 56　　**9** 167 – 82　　**10** 194 – 75
11 118 – 47

B

1 (a) 381, 619　　(b) 294, 456　　**2** 340　　　**3** 427
4　358　　　　　**5**　583　　　**6**　316　　　**7**　691
　　+ 205　　　　　　　+ 178　　　　　– 253　　　　　– 278

C

1 (a) 1823, 3177　(b) 1661, 2139　**2** 5658　　**3** 1194
4　1368　　　　　**5**　3473　　　**6**　4425　　**7**　5146
　　+ 2875　　　　　　　+ 1597　　　　　– 1679　　　　– 3748

Page 15

A

1 1, 6　　　　　**3** 1, 2, 3, 6　　　**5** 1, 2, 3, 4, 6, 12
6 1, 2, 5, 10　　**7** 1, 2, 3, 6, 9, 18

B

1

Number	No. of Arrays	Factors
10	2	1, 2, 5, 10
11	1	1, 11
12	3	1, 2, 3, 4, 6, 12
13	1	1, 13
14	2	1, 2, 7, 14
15	2	1, 3, 5, 15
16	3	1, 2, 4, 8, 16
17	1	1, 17
18	3	1, 2, 3, 6, 9, 18
19	1	1, 19
20	3	1, 2, 4, 5, 10, 20

2 16　　　　　　**5** 1, 3, 11, 33　　　**6** 1, 3, 5, 9, 15, 45
7 1, 3, 9　　　**8** 1, 2, 3, 4, 6, 8, 12, 24

C

1 1, 4, 9, 16, 25, 36, 49, 64, 81, 100
2 225　　　　　　　　　　**3** 400
4 10 000　　　　　　　　**5** 1, 2, 4, 5, 10, 20
6 1, 3, 11, 33　　　　　**7** 1, 2, 4, 8, 16, 32, 64
8 1, 3, 9, 27　　　　　　**9** 1, 2, 4, 5, 8, 10, 16, 20, 40, 80
10 1, 2, 13, 26　　　　　**11** 1, 2, 3, 6, 11, 22, 33, 66
12 1, 3, 9, 27, 81　　　　**13** 1, 3, 5, 9, 15, 45
14 1, 2, 4, 7, 8, 14, 28, 56　　**15** 1, 2, 3, 6, 13, 26, 39, 78
16 1, 2, 3, 4, 6, 8, 12, 16, 24, 32, 48, 96　**17** 8　　**18** 4
19 90　　**20** 5　　**21** 30　　**22** 50　　**23** 90　　**24** 8

Page 16

A

1

	odd	not odd
over 50	53 65 87	54 78 96
not over 50	31 37 45	16 22 48

2

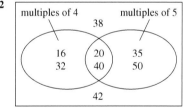

3 (a) 2, 4, 6, 8, 10, 12, 14, 16, 18, 20　　(b) 5, 10, 15, 20
　(c) 10, 20　　　(d) 10, 20, 30, 40, 50, 60, 70, 80, 90, 100

Page 17

B

1

	multiples of 5			not multiples of 5		
2-digit numbers	45	60	70	38	52	87
not 2-digit numbers	5	195	210	8	151	306

2

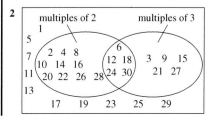

3 6, 12, 18, 24, 30   **4** 36, 42, 48, 54, 60, 66, 72, 78, 84, 90, 96
6 15, 30, 45, etc.   **7** 10, 20, 30, etc.   **8** 14, 28, 42, etc.
9 20, 40, 60, etc.   **10** 24, 48, 72, etc.

C

1
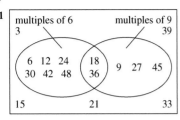

multiples of 6   multiples of 9
3   39

6 12 24   18   9 27 45
30 42 48   36

15   21   33

2

	multiples of 4			not multiples of 4		
multiples of 6	12	24	36	6	18	30
not multiples of 6	4 8 16			2 10 14		
	20 28 32			22 26 34		

3 12, 24, 36   **4** 12, 24, 36, 48, 60, 72, 84, 96
6 42, 84, 126, etc.   **7** 90, 180, 270, etc.   **8** 60, 120, 180, etc.
9 126, 252, 378, etc.   **10** 120, 240, 360, etc.

Page 18
A

1 18	**2** 36	**3** 28	**4** 42	**5** 25	**6** 42
7 40	**8** 54	**9** 14	**10** 24	**11** 27	**12** 56
13 8	**14** 2	**15** 6	**16** 8	**17** 9	**18** 5
19 6	**20** 8	**21** 7	**22** 5	**23** 9	**24** 7

B

1 12	**2** 8	**3** 4	**4** 5	**5** 9	**6** 8
7 20	**8** 21	**9** 24	**10** 24	**11** 32	**12** 63
13 180	**14** 720	**15** 4900	**16** 3200	**17** 270	**18** 3000
19 810	**20** 4000	**21** 4800	**22** 180	**23** 120	**24** 3500
25 600	**26** 90	**27** 800	**28** 900	**29** 70	**30** 300
31 4	**32** 90	**33** 6	**34** 6	**35** 90	**36** 70

C

1 20	**2** 700	**3** 900	**4** 300	**5** 70	**6** 400
7 3000	**8** 140	**9** 560	**10** 2400	**11** 4000	**12** 630
13 3.6	**14** 2.4	**15** 7.2	**16** 3.6	**17** 1.6	**18** 6.3
19 0.6	**20** 0.4	**21** 0.8	**22** 0.5	**23** 0.7	**24** 0.9
25 1.8	**26** 4.8	**27** 2.8	**28** 4.2	**29** 2.4	**30** 2.5
31 0.04	**32** 0.07	**33** 0.09	**34** 0.08	**35** 0.06	**36** 0.08

Page 19
A

1 60	**2** 30	**3** 30	**4** 50	**5** 80	**6** 100
7 70	**8** 20	**9** 40	**10** 70	**11** 800	**12** 200
13 500	**14** 300	**15** 300	**16** 700	**17** 500	**18** 700
19 300	**20** 900	**21** 429	**22** 327	**23** 589	**24** 608
25 31	**26** 26	**27** 48	**28** 52		

B

1 (b) 634   **2** (c) 4724   **3** 8514 − 3696
4 4693 + 2538   **5** 2974 + 3268   **6** 5328 − 1753
7 759   **8** 569   **9** 621   **10** 869   **11** 223   **12** 308
13 359   **14** 197

C

1 (b) 76.12   **2** (a) 14.27   **3** 494.8 + 367.5
4 722.5 − 548.8   **5** 83.17 − 26.49   **6** 46.36 + 20.59
7 661.3   **8** 799.8   **9** 38.93   **10** 65.18   **11** 172.1   **12** 310.7
13 40.34   **14** 7.85

Page 20
A

A	triangular based pyramid	B	pentagonal based prism
C	cylinder	D	sphere
E	triangular based prism	F	cone
G	square based pyramid	H	octagonal based prism
I	hemisphere	J	cube
K	hexagonal based prism	L	cuboid

B

1 (a) cone   (b) cube
     cylinder   cuboid
     hemisphere   hexagonal based prism
     sphere   octagonal based prism
                                                     pentagonal based prism
                                                     triangular based prism
  (c) square based pyramid   (d) cube
       triangular based prism   cuboid
  (e) pentagonal based prism (f) cube
       triangular based prism   triangular based pyramid
2 square based pyramid

C

1

Name	Faces	Edges	Vertices
cube	6	12	8
pentagonal prism	7	15	10
triangular pyramid	4	6	4
triangular prism	5	9	6
square pyramid	5	8	5
octagonal prism	10	24	16
cuboid	6	12	8
hexagonal prism	8	18	12

2 (a) 10 (b) 30   **3** (a) 9   (b) 9

Page 21
A

2 Yes   **3** All four lines are equal.   **4** Yes
5 (a) Yes   (b) Yes   (c) No

B

1 (a) not equal   (b) not bisect   (c) perpendicular
2 (a) not equal   (b) bisect   (c) not perpendicular
3 (a) not equal   (b) not bisect   (c) not perpendicular
4 (a) equal   (b) not bisect   (c) not perpendicular
5 (a) not equal   (b) not bisect   (c) not perpendicular
6 (a) not equal   (b) bisect   (c) perpendicular

Page 22
A

1 3 kg	**2** 1 kg	**3** 6 kg	**4** 4000 g	**5** 2000 g
6 7000 g	**7** 2.5 kg	**8** 3.5 kg	**9** 5.5 kg	**10** 6500 g
11 1500 g	**12** 4500 g	**13** g	**14** kg	**15** kg
16 g	**17** g	**18** kg		

B

1 8.6 kg	**2** 2.4 kg	**3** 0.8 kg	**4** 3100 g	**5** 1200 g
6 9700 g	**7** 5.3 kg	**8** 7.1 kg	**9** 6.4 kg	**10** 2900 g
11 8300 g	**12** 700 g	**13** kg	**14** g	**15** kg
16 g				

C

1 3.16 kg	**2** 0.39 kg	**3** 4.62 kg	**4** 8080 g	**5** 2750 g
6 5470 g	**7** 1.94 kg	**8** 6.16 kg	**9** 7.53 kg	**10** 220 g
11 2310 g	**12** 9850 g	**13** 3.5 kg	**14** 10 g	**15** 70 kg
16 0.4 kg				

Answers

Page 23

A

1

Length (minutes)	2	3	4	5	6
Number of tracks	1	8	6	4	1

2 (a) 6　　(b) 1　　**3** (a) 2 mins.　　(b) 6 mins.　　**7** 3 mins.

B

1

Age	7	8	9	10	11
Brownies	2	10	7	4	1

2 8　　　**3** 24

4

No. of letters	3	4	5	6	7	8	9
Total	2	4	5	7	6	3	1

5 6　　**6** 4

C

1

Temp.	6	7	8	9	10	11	12	13
Frequency	1	3	5	2	5	3	6	5

2 (a) 14　　(b) 11　　**3** 12ºC　　**4** 7ºC
5 4 mins.　　4 years　　6 letters

Page 25

B

1

Portions of Fruit and Veg.	0	1	2	3	4	5	6
Frequency	1	2	5	10	7	2	1

C

1

Weight (g)	Total
101–120	3
121–140	7
141–160	13
161–180	5
181–200	2

3 (b)

Desserts	Total
Cake	260
Fruit	230
Ice Cream	290
Yoghurt	300

Page 26

A

1 420　**2** 800　**3** 1360　**4** 570　**5** 20　**6** 92
7 300　**8** 78　**9** 2400　**10** 6000　**11** 700　**12** 9100
13 6　**14** 41　**15** 80　**16** 15　**17** 3000　**18** 12 000
19 5000　**20** 40 000　**21** 29　**22** 70　**23** 9　**24** 46
25 37　**26** 20　**27** 7　**28** 6400　**29** 1900　**30** 8000

B

1 460 × 100　　**2** 27 × 1000　　**3** 16 700 ÷ 10
4 9000 ÷ 100　　**5** 314 × 10　　**6** 18 × 100
7 65 000 ÷ 1000　**8** 16 700 ÷ 10
9 70 mm　**10** 20 mm　**11** 6 cm　**12** 10 cm　**13** 300 cm
14 1200 cm　**15** 0.9 m　**16** 2.4 m　**17** 5000 m　**18** 42 000 m
19 8 km　**20** 10 km

C

1 70 000 × 10　　**2** 3000 × 100　　**3** 260 × 1000
4 6200 × 10　　**5** 157 000 ÷ 100　**6** 347 000 ÷ 1000
7 493 000 ÷ 10　**8** 28 600 ÷ 100　**9** 39 mm
10 6 mm　**11** 11.7 cm　**12** 5.8 cm　**13** 180 cm
14 57 cm　**15** 2.43 m　**16** 0.09 m　**17** 2700 m
18 800 m　**19** 1.5 km　**20** 4.36 km

Page 27

A

1 1.43 m　**2** 1.15 m　**3** 5 m　**4** 25　**5** 4.8 km
6 9.7 cm　**7** 300 m

B

1 250 m　**2** 2.12 m　**3** 166 m　**4** 19.2 cm　**5** 30 m
6 1.66 m　**7** 2.24 m

C

1 92 cm　**2** 1.82 m　**3** 30　**4** 3.6 km　**5** 1147 m　**6** 8.4 cm

Page 28

A

1 (a) 1.7 cm　　(b) 4.4 cm　　(c) 6.8 cm　　(d) 9.3 cm
　(e) 12.1 cm　(f) 14.6 cm　**2** (g) 7 cm　　(h) 29 cm
　(i) 42 cm　　(j) 58 cm　　(k) 74 cm　　(l) 91 cm
3 9.7 cm　　**4** 12.3 cm　　**5** 8.5 cm　　**6** 14.6 cm
7 6.0 cm　　**8** 11.9 cm

Page 29

B

1 D (a) 6.8 cm, 2.7 cm　　(b) 19.0 cm
　E (a) 1.5 cm　　(b) 9.0 cm
　F (a) 5.2 cm, 3.6 cm, 1.8 cm, 2.0 cm, 3.4 cm, 1.6 cm　(b) 17.6 cm
　G (a) 3.3 cm, 2.2 cm　　(b) 11.0 cm
　H (a) 2.8 cm　　(b) 11.2 cm

C

1 J (a) 7.2 cm, 2.3 cm, 4.7 cm, 4.2 cm　　(b) 18.4 cm
　K (a) 4.4 cm, 2.6 cm, 1.9 cm, 3.7 cm, 3.8 cm　(b) 16.4 cm
　L (a) 1.6 cm　　(b) 8.0 cm
　M (a) 4.9 cm, 3.0 cm, 3.5 cm, 2.6 cm　(b) 14.0 cm
　N (a) 4.2 cm, 3.2 cm, 4.2 cm, 2.1 cm　(b) 13.7 cm

Page 30

B

Allow +/– 0.1 cm

1 7.1 cm　**2** 10 cm　**3** 4.9 cm or 5.0 cm　**4** 6 cm　**5** 6.5 cm

C

Allow +/– 0.1 cm
1 7.1 cm　**2** 11.3 cm　**3** 3.0 cm　**4** 9.2 cm　**5** 5.8 cm

Page 31

A

1 31　**2** 30　**3** 61　**4** 62
5 Not a leap year　**6** (a) Thursday　(b) Tuesday
　(c) Saturday　　(d) Sunday　　**7** 13th February
8 2nd November

B

1 6th May　**2** 2nd October　**3** 8th January　**4** 2nd November
5 Sunday　**6** Wednesday　**7** Friday　**8** Sunday
9　**10** Monday

APRIL						
Su	M	Tu	W	Th	F	Sa
					1	2
3	4	5	6	7	8	9
10	11	12	13	14	15	16
17	18	19	20	21	22	23
24	25	26	27	28	29	30

C

1 14th November　**2** 13th July　**3** 2nd January　**4** 30th April

5 Friday   **6** Sunday   **7** Sunday
8 52 weeks, 1 day left over   **9** Wednesday   **10** Friday

Page 32

A

	(a)	(b)
1	10 past 3	3:10 pm
2	3 mins. past 12	12:03 pm
3	6 mins. to 10	9:54 am
4	11 mins. to 5	4:49 am
5	25 past 2	2:25 am
6	12 mins. past 7	7:12 pm
7	23 mins. to 7	6:37 pm
8	2 mins. to 6	5.58 am
9	21 mins. past 1	1:21 pm
10	26 mins. to 4	3:34 am
11	quarter to 12	11:45 pm
12	23 mins. past 6	6:23 am
13	17 mins. past 2	2:17 am
14	8 mins. to 6	5:52 pm
15	22 mins. to 9	8:38 am
16	1 min. past 10	10:01 pm
17	3 mins. to 4	3:57 am
18	17 mins. to 10	9:43 pm
19	6 mins. past 7	7:06 am
20	quarter past 1	1:15 am

Page 33

B

1

TIME IN WORDS	12-HOUR	24-HOUR
quarter to 8	7:45 am	07:45
half past 8	8:30 pm	20:30
25 to 11	10:35 am	10:35
8 mins. to 4	3:52 am	03:52
24 mins. past 2	2:24 pm	14:24
8 mins. past 4	4:08 am	04:08
19 mins. past 10	10:19 pm	22:19
23 mins. to 10	9:37 am	09:37
16 mins. past 6	6:16 pm	18:16
28 mins. past 11	11:28 am	11:28
7 mins. to 7	6:53 pm	18:53
4 mins. past 1	1:04 am	01:04
12 mins. to 4	3:48 pm	15:48

2 15, 30, 25, 8, 36, 52, 41, 23, 44, 32, 7, 56, 12

C

	(a)	(b)	(c)
1	13 mins. to 9	8:47 am	08:47
2	23 mins. past 2	2:23 pm	14:23
3	1 min. to 1	12:59 am	00:59
4	28 mins. to 12	11:32 pm	23:32
5	6 mins. past 3	3:06 am	03:06
6	18 mins. past 11	11:18 am	11:18
7	4 mins. past 5	5:04 pm	17:04
8	23 mins. to 1	12:37 pm	12:37
9	27 mins. to 9	8:33 pm	20:33
10	21 mins. past 6	6:21 am	06:21

11   **i.** 15 hours 13 mins.   **ii.** 9 hours 37 mins.
   iii. 23 hours 1 min.   **iv.** 28 minutes
    v. 20 hours 54 mins.   **vi.** 12 hours 42 mins.
  vii. 6 hours 56 mins.   **viii.** 11 hours 23 mins.
   ix. 3 hours 27 mins.   **x.** 17 hours 39 mins.

12

	Jan. 2	March 6	May 1	July 3	Sept 4	Nov 6
Sunrise	08:06	06:36	05:34	04:49	06:17	07:02
Sunset	16:03	17:49	20:23	21:20	19:41	16:26
Daylight	7h 57m	11h 13m	14h 49m	16h 31m	13h 24m	9h 24m

Page 34

A

1 L	**2** Q	**3** O	**4** X	**5** J	**6** S
7 R	**8** P	**9** (0, 3)	**10** (3, 1)	**11** (1, 0)	**12** (5, 4)
13 (4, 3)	**14** (0, 5)	**15** (2, 4)	**16** (3, 2)		

B

5 B(7, 6)   D(2, 2)   **6** (10, 4)   **7** e.g. (4, 5) (10, 8)   (1, 2) (2, 4)
    (3, 6) (5, 10) etc   (8, 1) (9, 3) (11, 7) (12, 9) etc.

C

1 (6, 2)   **2** (10, 4) (8, 1)   **3** (a) (4, 5)   (b) (4, 0)   (c) (0, 2)

Page 35

A

1 27	**2** 14	**3** 48	**4** 54	**5** 40	**6** 14
7 18	**8** 30	**9** 63	**10** 36	**11** 56	**12** 32
13 6	**14** 7	**15** 2	**16** 8	**17** 6	**18** 4
19 8	**20** 9	**21** 3	**22** 6	**23** 8	**24** 5

B

1 9	**2** 4	**3** 7	**4** 5	**5** 9	**6** 8
7 18	**8** 49	**9** 54	**10** 27	**11** 12	**12** 24
13 240	**14** 4200	**15** 2400	**16** 450	**17** 56 000	**18** 2100
19 12 000	**20** 7200	**21** 160	**22** 35 000	**23** 6300	**24** 2400
25 400	**26** 90	**27** 80	**28** 70	**29** 5	**30** 70
31 8	**32** 200	**33** 900	**34** 70	**35** 30	**36** 60

C

1 30	**2** 70	**3** 60	**4** 400	**5** 6	**6** 700
7 1800	**8** 32000	**9** 420	**10** 3600	**11** 2700	**12** 40 000
13 2.4	**14** 6.3	**15** 1.6	**16** 7.2	**17** 7.2	**18** 1.8
19 4.5	**20** 1.6	**21** 4.5	**22** 2.8	**23** 2.4	**24** 4.2
25 0.9	**26** 0.7	**27** 0.8	**28** 0.5	**29** 0.9	**30** 0.7
31 0.6	**32** 0.4	**33** 0.8	**34** 0.6	**35** 0.3	**36** 0.8

Page 36

A

1 39	**2** 54	**3** 72	**4** 48	**5** 76	**6** 92
7 17	**8** 12	**9** 13	**10** 14	**11** 23	**12** 15
13 42	**14** 72	**15** 54	**16** 15	**17** 14	**18** 9

19 128 ÷ 16   **20** 64 ÷ 8   **21** 32 ÷ 4   **22** 16 ÷ 2

B

1 136	**2** 285	**3** 252	**4** 168	**5** 224	**6** 288
7 14	**8** 19	**9** 26	**10** 47	**11** 29	**12** 23
13 90	**14** 96	**15** 156	**16** 126	**17** 153	**18** 108
19 16	**20** 15	**21** 21	**22** 8	**23** 15	**24** 14

25 1200 ÷ 24   **26** 600 ÷ 12   **27** 300 ÷ 6   **28** 150 ÷ 3

C

1 62	**2** 17	**3** 43	**4** 23	**5** 44	**6** 26
7 48	**8** 300	**9** 357	**10** 312	**11** 243	**12** 450
13 9	**14** 18	**15** 17	**16** 15	**17** 18	**18** 30

19 2160 ÷ 36   **20** 1080 ÷ 18   **21** 540 ÷ 9   **22** 180 ÷ 3

Page 37

A

1 (a) 5, 6   (b) 6, 9   (c) 5, 9   (d) 4, 6   **2** (a) 54
    (b) 120   **3** 49, 64   **4** Yes   **5** Yes   **6** No
7 Yes   **8** 45   **9** 6   **10** 1, 2, 3, 4, 6, 9, 12, 18, 36
11 1, 2, 4, 23, 46, 92   **12** 21, 42, etc.

B

1 (a) 3, 5   (b) 7, 8   (c) 3, 7   (d) 3, 5, 8

2 (a) 280   (b) 105   **3** (a) 38, 57   (b) 58, 87
4 (a) 36, 72, etc.   (b) 65, 130, etc.
5 (a) 1, 2, 3, 4, 6, 8, 12, 16, 24, 48   (b) 1, 2, 4, 19, 38, 76
6 (a) 4   (b) 6   (c) 12   (d) 16
7 (a) 97   (b) 49   (c) 95

C

1 (a) 18   (b) 12   (c) 40   (d) 36
2 (a) 14   (b) 16   (c) 12   (d) 18
4 (a) 80   (b) 99   (c) 88   (d) 81
5 (a) 12, 72   (b) 12, 52, 72, 92
   (c) 12, 15, 21, 27, 51, 57, 72, 75

Page 38

A

1 117   **2** 116   **3** 102   **4** 144   **5** 112   **6** 140
7 138   **8** 315   **9** 208   **10** 348   **11** 336   **12** 270
13 378   **14** 630   **15** 377   **16** 690
17 (a) 35×7 37×5 53×7 57×3 73×5 75×3
   (b) 53×7 (c) 57×3

B

1 1458   **2** 2625   **3** 1512   **4** 1992   **5** 1840   **6** 2188
7 1806   **8** 990   **9** 782   **10** 700   **11** 1134   **12** 1344
13 2176   **14** 1634   **15** 2565   **16** 1950   **17** 22
18 (a) There are 24 different ways.   (b) 42×91 or 91×42
   (c) 14×29 or 29×14

C

1 3694   **2** 11 168   **3** 12 685   **4** 14 583
5 13 552   **6** 23 832   **7** 8094   **8** 22 072
9 2432   **10** 6422   **11** 5814   **12** 13 870
13 8640   **14** 7848   **15** 13 468   **16** 10 206
17 71   **18** (a) 9801   (b) 9702   **19** (a) 17×18
(b) 33×34 (c) 56×57 (d) 92×93

Page 39

A

1 $\frac{1}{4} = \frac{2}{8}$ **2** $\frac{1}{5} = \frac{2}{10}$ **3** $\frac{1}{3} = \frac{4}{12}$ **4** $\frac{9}{10} = \frac{90}{100}$
5 $\frac{1}{3} = \frac{2}{6}$ **6** $\frac{1}{2} = \frac{3}{6}$ **7** $\frac{2}{3} = \frac{6}{9}$

B

1 $\frac{4}{16}$ **2** $\frac{4}{8}$ **3** $\frac{2}{16}$ **4** $\frac{6}{8}$ **5** $\frac{10}{16}$ **6** $\frac{8}{16}$
7 $\frac{8}{16}$ **8** $\frac{6}{16}$ **9** $\frac{2}{4}$ **10** $\frac{2}{8}$ **11** $\frac{14}{16}$ **12** $\frac{12}{16}$
13 $\frac{6}{9}$ **14** $\frac{10}{12}$ **15** $\frac{2}{6}$ **16** $\frac{8}{12}$ **17** $\frac{4}{6}$ **18** $\frac{6}{9}$
19 $\frac{1}{3}$ **20** $\frac{3}{9}$ **21** $\frac{1}{6}$ **22** $\frac{2}{3}$ **23** $\frac{2}{6}$ **24** $\frac{1}{3}$

C

1 $\frac{4}{10}$ **2** $\frac{12}{16}$ **3** $\frac{70}{100}$ **4** $\frac{3}{18}$ **5** $\frac{76}{100}$ **6** $\frac{10}{14}$
7 $\frac{2}{3}$ **8** $\frac{3}{5}$ **9** $\frac{1}{2}$ **10** $\frac{4}{20}$ **11** $\frac{1}{3}$ **12** $\frac{3}{4}$
13 $\frac{12}{16}, \frac{15}{20}, \frac{18}{24}$ **14** $\frac{4}{24}, \frac{5}{30}, \frac{6}{36}$ **15** $\frac{8}{20}, \frac{10}{25}, \frac{12}{30}$
16 $\frac{4}{32}, \frac{5}{40}, \frac{6}{48}$ **17** $\frac{8}{12}, \frac{10}{15}, \frac{12}{18}$ **18** $\frac{36}{40}, \frac{45}{50}, \frac{54}{60}$
19 e.g. $\frac{10}{26}, \frac{15}{39}, \frac{20}{52}$, etc.   **20** e.g. $\frac{2}{9}, \frac{4}{18}, \frac{6}{27}$, etc.
21 e.g. $\frac{5}{12}, \frac{15}{36}, \frac{20}{48}$, etc.   **22** e.g. $\frac{6}{11}, \frac{12}{22}, \frac{24}{44}$, etc.
23 e.g. $\frac{18}{32}, \frac{27}{48}, \frac{36}{64}$, etc.   **24** e.g. $\frac{7}{8}, \frac{14}{16}, \frac{21}{24}$, etc.
25 e.g. $\frac{7}{15}, \frac{14}{30}, \frac{21}{45}$, etc.   **26** e.g. $\frac{7}{25}, \frac{14}{50}, \frac{21}{75}$, etc.

Page 40

A

1 5×2 **2** $\frac{1}{5}$ of 10   **3** 3×3 **4** $\frac{1}{3}$ of 9   **5** 2×4
6 $\frac{1}{2}$ of 8   **7** 3×2 **8** $\frac{1}{3}$ of 6   **9** 4×3 **10** $\frac{1}{4}$ of 12

B

1 (a) $\frac{1}{5}$ (b) $\frac{1}{3}$ (c) $\frac{2}{5}$ (d) $\frac{2}{3}$
2 (a) $\frac{1}{4}$ (b) $\frac{3}{4}$ (c) $\frac{1}{8}$ (d) $\frac{3}{8}$
3 (a) $\frac{1}{10}$ (b) $\frac{1}{4}$ (c) $\frac{7}{20}$ (d) $\frac{4}{5}$
4 (a) $\frac{1}{20}$ (b) $\frac{1}{5}$ (c) $\frac{1}{4}$ (d) $\frac{3}{4}$
5 (a) $\frac{1}{24}$ (b) $\frac{1}{6}$ (c) $\frac{1}{4}$ (d) $\frac{1}{3}$

C

1 (a) $\frac{1}{10}$ (b) $\frac{1}{5}$ (c) $\frac{3}{5}$ (d) $\frac{9}{10}$
2 (a) $\frac{1}{6}$ (b) $\frac{1}{12}$ (c) $\frac{5}{12}$ (d) $\frac{1}{5}$
3 (a) $\frac{1}{6}$ (b) $\frac{1}{4}$ (c) $\frac{3}{4}$ (d) $\frac{5}{8}$
4 (a) $\frac{1}{50}$ (b) $\frac{9}{20}$ (c) $\frac{99}{100}$ (d) $\frac{3}{25}$
5 (a) $\frac{1}{50}$ (b) $\frac{1}{8}$ (c) $\frac{4}{5}$ (d) $\frac{1}{20}$
6 $\frac{1}{8}, \frac{7}{8}$ **7** $\frac{7}{8}$

Page 41

A

1 5   **2** 3   **3** 6   **4** 4   **5** 3   **6** 8
7 2 p   **8** 5 p   **9** 2   **10** 6   **11** 5 cm   **12** 9 cm
13 3   **14** 9   **15** £10   **16** £4   **17** 2   **18** 8
19 5 m   **20** 9 m

B

1 6   **2** 18   **3** 4   **4** 12   **5** 10   **6** 40
7 7   **8** 14   **9** 10   **10** 14   **11** 12   **12** 63
13 20 p   **14** 21 p   **15** £10   **16** £16   **17** 25 cm   **18** 14 cm
19 15 m   **20** 12 m

C

1 84 cm   **2** £30   **3** 14 litres   **4** 45 cm   **5** £4.50   **6** 42
7 240 g   **8** 842 m   **9** 240 g   **10** 40   **11** 1.75 litres   **12** 16 mins.

Page 42

A

1 8 cm, 32 cm   **2** 15   **3** 40   **4** 27
5 (a) 8   (b) 6   (c) 10

B

1 9   **2** 300 ml   **3** 14 cm, 21 cm   **4** 40kg
5 117 miles   **6** 1280 yards   **7** 192

C

1 280g   **2** 10 746   **3** 3.125kg   **4** 325 ml
5 76   **6** 40 cm

Page 43

A

1 2.7   **2** 5.4   **3** 1.3   **4** 0.8   **5** 9.1   **6** 4.6
7 7.9   **8** 0.7   **9** 3.2   **10** 6.5   **11** 8.8   **12** 0.3
13 $2\frac{1}{10}$ **14** $\frac{6}{10}$ **15** $1\frac{2}{10}$ **16** $5\frac{9}{10}$ **17** $\frac{5}{10}$ **18** $2\frac{8}{10}$
19 $7\frac{3}{10}$ **20** $3\frac{7}{10}$ **21** $\frac{1}{10}$ **22** $9\frac{5}{10}$ **23** $6\frac{4}{10}$ **24** $\frac{2}{10}$

25 0.3   **26** 0.2   **27** 0.1   **28** 0.6   **29** 0.4   **30** 0.2
31 0.5   **32** 0.2   **33** 0.6   **34** 0.4

B

1 $8 + 0.4 + 0.07$ **2** $2 + 0.2 + 0.03$ **3** $0.9 + 0.01$
4 $1 + 0.07$ **5** $5 + 0.7 + 0.03$ **6** $4 + 0.3 + 0.08$
7 $7 + 0.8 + 0.02$ **8** $3 + 0.4 + 0.06$ **9** $20 + 0.08$
10 $9 + 0.9 + 0.04$ **11** $5 + 0.2 + 0.09$ **12** $0.6 + 0.05$
13 $4 + \frac{6}{10} + \frac{3}{100}$ **14** $7 + \frac{4}{10} + \frac{5}{100}$ **15** $\frac{1}{10} + \frac{2}{100}$
16 $3 + \frac{7}{10} + \frac{7}{100}$ **17** $5 + \frac{9}{100}$ **18** $\frac{2}{10} + \frac{1}{100}$
19 $7 + \frac{6}{100}$ **20** $11 + \frac{4}{10} + \frac{3}{100}$ **21** $4 + \frac{4}{100}$
22 $23 + \frac{6}{10} + \frac{2}{100}$ **23** $\frac{5}{10} + \frac{8}{100}$ **24** $6 + \frac{9}{10} + \frac{5}{100}$
25 $3.23 + 0.03$ **26** $1.37 + 0.5$ **27** $0.65 + 0.02$
28 $4.12 + 0.6$ **29** $6.73 + 0.07$ **30** $0.51 - 0.2$
31 $2.76 - 0.05$ **32** $8.93 - 0.6$ **33** $1.82 - 0.3$
34 $0.68 - 0.04$

C

1 2.761   **2** 5.239   **3** 8.014   **4** 0.608   **5** 7.356   **6** 4.901
7 $2 + \frac{4}{10} + \frac{7}{100} + \frac{5}{1000}$ **8** $5 + \frac{8}{10} + \frac{2}{100} + \frac{1}{1000}$
9 $3 + \frac{8}{100} + \frac{3}{1000}$ **10** $\frac{1}{10} + \frac{4}{100} + \frac{6}{1000}$
11 $1 + \frac{9}{10} + \frac{4}{1000}$ **12** $8 + \frac{5}{10} + \frac{1}{100} + \frac{2}{1000}$
13 $3 + \frac{6}{10} + \frac{3}{100} + \frac{9}{1000}$ **14** $\frac{2}{10} + \frac{7}{1000}$
15 $5 + \frac{6}{100} + \frac{1}{1000}$ **16** $\frac{4}{10} + \frac{9}{100} + \frac{6}{1000}$
17 $4 + \frac{3}{10} + \frac{5}{100} + \frac{8}{1000}$ **18** $6 + \frac{7}{10} + \frac{2}{1000}$
19 0.005   **20** 0.03   **21** 0.008   **22** 0.2   **23** 0.06   **24** 0.2
25 0.005   **26** 0.01   **27** 0.9   **28** 0.007

Page 44
A

1 $\frac{9}{10}$, 0.9   **2** $\frac{1}{10}$, 0.1   **3** $\frac{5}{10}$, 0.5   **4** $\frac{10}{10}$, 1.0
5 $\frac{6}{10}$, 0.6   **6** $\frac{3}{10}$, 0.3   **7** $\frac{2}{10}$, 0.2   **8** $\frac{7}{10}$, 0.7
9 A 1.3   B 1.6   C 1.8   D 2.2   E 2.5   F 2.9
10 0.4   **11** 1.7   **12** 3.3   **13** 2.9   **14** 6.8   **15** 0.6
16 10.5   **17** 17.2   **18** 4.1

Page 45
B

1 $\frac{16}{100}$, 0.16   **2** $\frac{93}{100}$, 0.93   **3** $\frac{8}{100}$, 0.08   **4** $\frac{65}{100}$, 0.65
5 A 0.12   B 0.14   C 0.18   D 0.23   E 0.25   F 0.29
6 G 1.1   H 1.2   I 1.35   J 1.65   K 1.8   L 1.95
7 $\frac{5}{10}$ **8** 8   **9** 40   **10** 6   **11** $\frac{2}{100}$ **12** $\frac{9}{10}$
13 $\frac{1}{10}$ **14** $\frac{2}{100}$ **15** $\frac{4}{10}$ **16** $\frac{5}{100}$ **17** $\frac{1}{100}$ **18** $\frac{2}{10}$
19 0.06, 0.07, 0.08, 0.09, 0.1   **20** 1.1, 1.12, 1.14, 1.16, 1.18
21 1.97, 1.98, 1.99, 2.0, 2.01   **22** 1.01, 1.03, 1.05, 1.07, 1.09
23 0.85, 0.9, 0.95, 1.0, 1.05   **24** 4.02, 4.01, 4.0, 3.99, 3.98

C

1 1.652   **2** 3.207   **3** 0.546   **4** 5.013   **5** 0.461   **6** 4.204
7 $1 + \frac{4}{10} + \frac{1}{100} + \frac{7}{1000}$ **8** 0.328   **9** $\frac{9}{10} + \frac{6}{1000}$
10 $5 + \frac{3}{100} + \frac{2}{1000}$ **11** 0.03   **12** 0.263   **13** 1.18   **14** 5.169
15 0.072   **16** 0.451   **17** 2.096   **18** 6.09   **19** 1.316   **20** $\frac{6}{10}$
21 $\frac{7}{10}$ **22** $\frac{5}{1000}$ **23** 6   **24** $\frac{1}{10}$ **25** $\frac{3}{100}$ **26** $\frac{8}{1000}$
27 9   **28** $\frac{6}{100}$

Page 46
A

1 5   **2** 24   **3** 0.5   **4** 17.2   **5** 3   **6** 9.1
7 36   **8** 21.8   **9** 50.9   **10** 2   **11** 68   **12** 4.3
13 3.2   **14** 0.6   **15** 0.15   **16** 0.04   **17** 7.6   **18** 0.25
19 0.08   **20** 0.8   **21** 0.41   **22** 0.03   **23** 9.9   **24** 0.5
25 0.7   **26** 0.16   **27** 4.09   **28** 5.2   **29** 8   **30** 0.3
31 15   **32** 2.9

B

1 1.5   **2** 14   **3** 203   **4** 20   **5** 6   **6** 580
7 339   **8** 70   **9** 1400   **10** 2   **11** 6170   **12** 500
13 0.09   **14** 4.72   **15** 0.003   **16** 18.5   **17** 0.63   **18** 0.041
19 0.007   **20** 45.3   **21** 0.016   **22** 0.02   **23** 1.306   **24** 0.158
25 2.69   **26** 7400   **27** 6.1   **28** 3580   **29** 0.7×1000
30 $0.8 \div 10$ **31** 9.01×10 **32** $10 \div 1000$

C

1 8.5   **2** 9   **3** 7.11   **4** 3.05   **5** 0.46   **6** 52
7 6.3×100 **8** $2.8 \div 10$ **9** 0.57×1000
10 $4.6 \div 100$ **11** 0.04×10 **12** $30 \div 1000$
13 0.02   **14** 0.005   **15** 0.1   **16** 0.9   **17** 25   **18** 500

Page 47
A

1 8.4   **2** 12.9   **3** 10.3   **4** 26.6   **5** 52.9
6 61.2   **7** 48.2   **8** 16.1   **9** 48.0   **10** 54.5
11 20.3 km   **12** 57.2 litres
B
1 82.2   **2** 7.32   **3** 15.18   **4** 12.55   **5** 107.7
6 7.01   **7** 20.33   **8** 4.60   **9** 36.42   **10** 105.4
11 62.05 kg   **12** £10.04   **13** 54.83 metres

C

1 67.4   **2** 9.83   **3** 99.34   **4** 15.51   **5** 18.12
6 49.52   **7** 672.33   **8** 2.21   **9** 23.24   **10** 49.19
11 30.73 litres   **12** 65.15 km

Page 48
A

1 138   **2** 36   **3** 409   **4** 224   **5** 523   **6** 217
7 416   **8** 139   **9** 364   **10** 274   **11** £657

B

1 17.6   **2** 32.6   **3** 13.1   **4** 9.1   **5** 64.4   **6** 3.71
7 1.54   **8** 4.38   **9** 2.86   **10** 0.72   **11** 27.9 kg   **12** £4.66
13 0.78 m

C

1 24.51   **2** 71.53   **3** 54.09   **4** 1.063   **5** 154.7   **6** 35.7
7 2.568   **8** 12.69   **9** 3.08   **10** 183.4   **11** 66.85   **12** 2.086
13 22.67 seconds   **14** £57.34

Page 49
A

1 12   **2** 32   **3** 24   **4** 45   **5** 35   **6** 56
7 48   **8** 28   **9** 42   **10** 27   **11** 36   **12** 40
13 6   **14** 5   **15** 8   **16** 4   **17** 9   **18** 3
19 5   **20** 7   **21** 5   **22** 6   **23** 8   **24** 6

B

1 7   **2** 8   **3** 9   **4** 5   **5** 3   **6** 7
7 16   **8** 36   **9** 45   **10** 63   **11** 32   **12** 21
13 270   **14** 1200   **15** 7200   **16** 490   **17** 150   **18** 4200

Answers

19 2700 **20** 300 **21** 630 **22** 4800 **23** 4000 **24** 630
25 30 **26** 600 **27** 90 **28** 900 **29** 600 **30** 80
31 50 **32** 7 **33** 20 **34** 6 **35** 40 **36** 90

C

1 80 **2** 40 **3** 600 **4** 50 **5** 7 **6** 70
7 560 **8** 1800 **9** 420 **10** 3200 **11** 450 **12** 4500
13 7.2 **14** 3.2 **15** 2.1 **16** 2.4 **17** 1.6 **18** 6.3
19 0.6 **20** 0.9 **21** 0.7 **22** 0.6 **23** 0.8 **24** 0.7
25 4.9 **26** 2.4 **27** 1.8 **28** 3.0 **29** 6.4 **30** 2.7
31 0.9 **32** 0.6 **33** 0.9 **34** 0.8 **35** 0.6 **36** 0.3

Page 50

A

1 125 **2** 32 **3** 132 **4** 171 **5** 224 **6** 120
7 116 **8** 116 **9** 72 **10** 81 **11** 170 miles

B

1 300 **2** 343 **3** 496 **4** 348 **5** 230 **6** 666
7 117 **8** 576 **9** 174 **10** 465 **11** 444 **12** 245
13 531 **14** 216 **15** 360 **16** 476 **17** 288 **18** 306 g
19 258 **20** £4.75

C

1 258 **2** 708 **3** 1724 **4** 1365 **5** 822 **6** 672
7 1035 **8** 840 **9** 1288 **10** 1888 **11** 2043 **12** 2304
13 1799 **14** 1737 **15** 1480 **16** 1590 **17** £2872 **18** 756 g
19 £1828

Page 51

A

1 13 r 1 **2** 14 r 2 **3** 15 r 3 **4** 12 r 2 **5** 18
6 17 r 4 **7** 11 r 2 **8** 12 **9** 15 r 1 **10** 18 r 1
11 14 r 3 **12** 13 r 1 **13** 18 r 3 **14** 13 **15** 17 r 1
16 11 r 4 **17** 19 **18** £17.50 **19** 64 **20** 16.25 m

B

1 17 r 1 **2** 16 r 2 **3** 24 r 2 **4** 17 **5** 19 r 2
6 16 r 6 **7** 24 r 1 **8** 18 **9** 23 r 3 **10** 18 r 4
11 31 r 1 **12** 19 r 4 **13** 24 r 3 **14** 16 r 7 **15** 42 r 1
16 17 r 4 **17** 18 **18** £12.25 **19** 125 miles **20** £34.40

C

1 23 **2** 32 **3** 25 r 2 **4** 54 r 2 **5** 31 r 5
6 65 r 3 **7** 48 r 4 **8** 23 r 1 **9** 36 **10** 57 r 2
11 28 **12** 47 **13** 35 r 3 **14** 74 **15** 49 r 2
16 56 r 8 **17** 136 **18** £27.75 **19** 448 **20** 71

Page 52

A

1 1 and 6, 2 and 3 **2** 2 and 4, 1 and 8
3 14 and 1, 7 and 2 **4** 5 and 3, 1 and 15
5 1 and 27, 3 and 9 **6** 30 and 1, 2 and 15, 3 and 10, 5 and 6
7 1 and 20, 2 and 10, 4 and 5 **8** 1 and 12, 2 and 6, 3 and 4
9 1 and 16, 2 and 8, 4 and 4
10 1 and 40, 2 and 20, 4 and 10, 5 and 8

B

1 1, 3, 7, 21 **2** 1, 2, 3, 6, 9, 18
3 1, 2, 3, 4, 6, 9, 12, 18, 36 **4** 1, 2, 3, 6, 9, 18, 27, 54
5 1, 2, 4, 7, 14, 28 **6** 1, 2, 3, 4, 6, 8, 12, 16, 24, 48
7 1, 7, 11, 77 **8** 1, 2, 4, 5, 8, 10, 16, 20, 40, 80
9 144 **10** 120 **11** 192 **12** 294 **13** 15 **14** 6
15 6 **16** 4 **17** 7 and 50 **18** 3 and 40 **19** 20 and 9
20 40 and 6 **21** 80 and 3 **22** 5 and 90

C

1 1, 2, 4, 8, 16, 32, 64 **2** 1, 2, 4, 5, 10, 20, 25, 50, 100
3 1, 2, 3, 4, 5, 6, 8, 10, 12, 15, 20, 24, 30, 40, 60, 120
4 1, 2, 3, 4, 6, 11, 12, 22, 33, 44, 66, 132
5 1, 2, 3, 6, 17, 34, 51, 102
6 1, 2, 4, 5, 8, 10, 20, 25, 40, 50, 100, 200
7 1, 2, 3, 4, 6, 9, 12, 18, 27, 36, 54, 108
8 1, 2, 4, 5, 8, 10, 16, 20, 32, 40, 80, 160
9 1, 5, 25, 125
10 1, 2, 3, 6, 11, 18, 33, 66, 99, 198
11 324 **12** 768 **13** 1150 **14** 1476 **15** 14 **16** 16
17 7 **18** 13 **19** 4 **20** 3 **21** 10 **22** 5
23 6 **24** 8 **25** 7 **26** 6 **27** 18 **28** 12

Page 53

A

1 4, 8, 12, 16, 20 **2** 5, 10, 15, 20, 25 **3** 10, 20, 30, 40, 50
4 6, 12, 18, 24, 30 **5** 9, 18, 27, 36, 45 **6** 20, 40, 60, 80, 100
7 Yes **8** No **9** Yes **10** No **11** No **12** Yes
13 Yes **14** Yes **15** Yes **16** No **17** Yes **18** Yes
19 No **20** Yes **21** No **22** Yes **23** Yes **24** No

B

1 106 **2** 54 **3** 46 **4** 69
5 14, 28, etc. **6** 12, 24, etc. **7** 15, 30, etc. **8** 20, 40, etc.
9 30, 60, etc. **10** 12, 24, etc. **11** 35, 70, etc. **12** 22, 44, etc.
13 6 **14** 24 **15** 12 **16** 20 **17** 15 **18** 24
19 30 **20** 18

C

1 18, 36, 54, etc. **2** 24, 48, 72, etc. **3** 40, 80, 120, etc.
4 28, 56, 84, etc. **5** 30, 60, 90, etc. **6** 24, 48, 72, etc.
7 42, 84, 126, etc. **8** 45, 90, 135, etc.
9 22 **10** 39 **11** 12 **12** 36 **13** 60 **14** 60
15 24 **16** 45
17 12, 16, 18, 26, 28, 32, 36, 38, 52, 56, 58, 62, 68, 82, 86
18 12, 15, 18, 21, 36, 51, 63, 81 **19** 15, 25, 35, 65, 85
20 16, 32, 56 **21** 21, 28, 35, 56, 63 **22** 18, 36, 63, 81
23 12, 16, 28, 32, 36, 52, 56, 68 **24** 12, 18, 36
25 27 and 90

Page 54

A

1 8.4 + 1.6 **2** 6.3 – 5 **3** 480 ÷ 6 **4** 12 × 9
5 56 **6** 9 **7** 720 **8** £4.86

B

1 £1.74 + £3.26 **2** 7.2 ÷ 9 **3** 25 × 16
4 10 – 6.22 **5** 0.5 × 7 **6** 167 + 96
7 1.05 – 0.15 **8** 31.8 ÷ 6 **9** 175 (176 if this is a Leap Year)
10 16 **11** 142 **12** Kirsty £10.00 **13** Pru £7.40

C

1 6.3 – 0.75 **2** 4 × 4.5 **3** 2.58 + 2.61 **4** 12 ÷ 20
5 17 × 17 **6** 5.37 – 1.27 **7** 0.175 + 0.325 **8** 86.4 ÷ 24
9 1500 **10** 2307 **11** 229 **12** 134

Page 55

A

1 37 **2** 63 **3** 63 **4** 260 **5** 2.6 **6** 630
7 0.26 **8** 6.3 **9** 34 **10** 3.4 **11** 70 **12** 700
13 58 **14** 0.58 **15** 92 **16** 9200 **17** 16 **18** 1.6
19 23 **20** 230 **21** 37 **22** 0.37 **23** 26 **24** 2600

B

1 8.3	**2** 0.34	**3** 620	**4** 4200	**5** 1.23	**6** 3.7
7 8400	**8** 270	**9** 10.2	**10** 0.47	**11** 10.4	**12** 1340
13 1.18	**14** 13 000	**15** 1680	**16** 1.52	**17** 7400	**18** 1.86
19 460	**20** 4.2	**21** 0.74	**22** 8100	**23** 0.28	**24** 790
25 6.4	**26** 9800				

C

1 0.26 + 0.46   **2** 9.1 – 3.2   **3** 3300 + 4200   **4** 970 – 440
5 6.6 + 4.7   **6** 0.8 – 0.41   **7** 160 + 8240   **8** 6200 – 2400
9 0.59 + 0.17   **10** 1.07 – 0.25   **11** 7.3   **12** 970
13 0.69   **14** 7600   **15** 5.7   **16** 1100   **17** 1.32
18 19.4   **19** 16 600   **20** 1.98

Page 56

A

1 16	**2** 28	**3** 28	**4** 30	**5** 54	**6** 45
7 81	**8** 40	**9** 21	**10** 32	**11** 36	**12** 18
13 9	**14** 6	**15** 8	**16** 7	**17** 4	**18** 6
19 5	**20** 7	**21** 8	**22** 9	**23** 7	**24** 5

B

1 6	**2** 9	**3** 7	**4** 4	**5** 6	**6** 7
7 24	**8** 54	**9** 56	**10** 40	**11** 18	**12** 42
13 2400	**14** 4500	**15** 350	**16** 7200	**17** 27 000	
18 4800	**19** 1200	**20** 56 000	**21** 300	**22** 70	
23 60	**24** 900	**25** 4	**26** 70	**27** 90	**28** 500

C

1 40	**2** 900	**3** 70	**4** 5	**5** 9	**6** 60
7 4800	**8** 180	**9** 4900	**10** 45 000	**11** 3600	**12** 48 000
13 5.6	**14** 2.5	**15** 6.3	**16** 2.4	**17** 0.54	**18** 0.14
19 0.3	**20** 0.56	**21** 0.6	**22** 0.9	**23** 0.6	**24** 0.8
25 0.09	**26** 0.06	**27** 0.08	**28** 0.06		

Page 57

A

2 1, 2, 4, 8   **4** 1, 3, 5, 15   **6** 1, 2, 4
8 1, 2, 4, 5, 10, 20   **9** 1 and 14, 2 and 7
10 1 and 18, 2 and 9, 3 and 6   **11** 1 and 22, 2 and 11
12 1 and 27, 3 and 9   **13** 1 and 28, 2 and 14, 4 and 7
14 1 and 32, 2 and 16, 4 and 8
15 1 and 40, 2 and 20, 4 and 10, 5 and 8
16 1 and 54, 2 and 27, 3 and 18, 6 and 9

B

1 1, 2, 17, 34   **2** 1, 2, 4, 13, 26, 52   **3** 1, 5, 25
4 1, 59   **5** 1, 2, 5, 7, 10, 14, 35, 70
6 1, 3, 7, 9, 21, 63   **7** 1, 5, 11, 55
8 1, 2, 3, 4, 6, 7, 12, 14, 21, 28, 42, 84
9 700 × 6   **10** 40 × 5   **11** 80 × 9   **12** 600 × 4
13 1 and 36, 2 and 18, 3 and 12, 4 and 9, 6 and 6
14 1 and 44, 2 and 22, 4 and 11
15 1 and 80, 2 and 40, 4 and 20, 5 and 16, 8 and 10
16 1 and 48, 2 and 24, 3 and 16, 4 and 12, 6 and 8

C

1 15	**2** 13	**3** 8	**4** 21
5 90 × 70	**6** 800 × 3	**7** 800 × 7	**8** 9 × 900

9 1 and 2200   2 and 1100   4 and 550   5 and 440
8 and 275   10 and 220   20 and 110   25 and 88
40 and 55   44 and 50
10 1 and 600   2 and 300   3 and 200   4 and 150
5 and 120   6 and 100   8 and 750   10 and 60
12 and 50   15 and 40   20 and 30   24 and 25

11 1 and 320   2 and 160   4 and 80   5 and 64
8 and 40   10 and 32   16 and 20
12 1 and 4900   2 and 2450   4 and 1225   5 and 980
7 and 700   10 and 490   14 and 350   20 and 245
25 and 196   28 and 175   35 and 140   49 and 100
50 and 98   70 and 70

Page 59

A

1 55	**2** 72	**3** £1.70	**4** 225 g	**5** 16

B

1 5	**2** 231	**3** 4	**4** 32	**5** 1.35 m	**6** £3.25

C

1 61 737	**2** 156	**3** 18 000	**4** 25	**5** £12.64	**6** 18

Page 60

B

5 e.g. The number of lines of symmetry in a regular polygon equals the number of sides.

C

5 The angles are equal.

Page 61

A

A cuboid   B cylinder
C tetrahedron   D hexagonal based prism
E cube   F pentagonal based prism
G cone   H octagonal based prism
I square based pyramid   J hemisphere
K triangular based prism   L octahedron

B

1 A cuboid   D hexagonal based prism
E cube   H octagonal based prism
2 F pentagonal based prism   K triangular based prism
3 I square based pyramid
4 C tetrahedron   L octahedron
5 all the faces   **6** the base
7 rectangular side faces   **8** all the faces
9 tetrahedron   **10** octahedron

C

1 8	**2** 12	**3** 7	**4** octahedron	**5** 0
6 0	**7** 7	**8** 10	**9** (a) 9	(b) 12

Page 62

C

1 (a) 2   (b) 3   **2** (a) 3 pairs   (b) 6 pairs

Page 63

A

1 2 litres	**2** 5 litres	**3** 1 litre	**4** 3000 ml
5 4000 ml	**6** 8000 ml	**7** 6.5 litres	**8** 0.5 litres
9 7.5 litres	**10** 3500 ml	**11** 1500 ml	**12** 9500 ml
13 litres	**14** ml	**15** ml	**16** litres	**17** litres	**18** ml

B

1 4.3 litres	**2** 1.7 litres	**3** 0.9 litres	**4** 7100 ml
5 2600 ml	**6** 5300 ml	**7** 9.2 litres	**8** 6.7 litres

9 3.8 litres   **10** 1400 ml   **11** 8100 ml   **12** 300 ml
13 litres   **14** ml   **15** ml   **16** ml   **17** litres   **18** litres

C

1 3.53 litres   **2** 0.86 litres   **3** 2.29 litres   **4** 5010 ml
5 2600 ml   **6** 7120 ml   **7** 1.58 litres   **8** 6.94 litres
9 4.31 litres   **10** 2070 ml   **11** 5630 ml   **12** 740 ml
13 0.15 litres   **14** 10 000 ml   **15** 0.3 litres   **16** 40 litres
17 250 ml   **18** 100 litres

Page 64
A

1 (a) 11   (b) Spain   (c) Italy   (d) 3   (e) 46

Page 65
B

1 (a) 4   (b) 9   (c) 4   (d) 15   (e) 31
(f) 50   **2** Approximate answers   (a) 80   (b) 26
(c) 8.6   (d) 5.7

C

1 (a) approx. 8:30   (b) 13°C   (c) 15°C   (d) –2°C
(e) 5 hours   (f) 3 hours

Page 67
B

11 (a) unlikely   (b) impossible   (c) likely
(d) unlikely   (e) unlikely   (f) likely
12 (a) likely   (b) unlikely   (c) impossible
(d) unlikely   (e) unlikely   (f) evens

C

1 Number line from 0 to 1 (with $\frac{1}{2}$ marked): c, e, g/h (with a, d above), f, b

2 Number line from 0 to 1 (with $\frac{1}{2}$ marked): c, d, f, e (with a above), b

3 Number line from 0 to 1: b/f, a, d, e, c, g

Page 68
A

1 75 ml   **2** Waqar   **3** 400 ml
4 Hugh was not right.   He drank less than 500 ml on both Wednesday and Thursday.
5 Ryan was not right.   He drank 540 ml on Wednesday.

B

1 (a) Thursday   (b) Tuesday   **2** Adele, Sanya   **3** Monday
4 Adele
5 The totals of water drunk were:
Tuesday 3545 ml
Friday 3505 ml.
It could be argued that this supports Sanya's statement or that the difference is not large enough to be significant.

6

Name	Adele	Hugh	Poppy	Ryan	Sanya	Waqar
Total no. of drinks	30	55	30	35	20	45

C

1 Poppy, Ryan   **2** 100 ml   **3** (a) 3 litres   (b) 2.75 litres
4 Sanya drank 250 ml on Monday and Waqar drank 825 ml on Thursday.   **5** Waqar

6

Day	Monday	Tuesday	Wednesday	Thursday	Friday
Amount Drunk	675 ml	750 ml	525 ml	825 ml	600 ml

Page 69
A

1 400   **2** 910   **3** 2800   **4** 65   **5** 9000
6 70   **7** 5110   **8** 83   **9** 16 400   **10** 200
11 34 000   **12** 21   **13** 9600   **14** 400   **15** 9000
16 193   **17** 20 000   **18** 50   **19** 8000   **20** 152
21 80 100   **22** 600   **23** 68 000   **24** 47

B

1 32   **2** 0.06   **3** 9   **4** 10.8   **5** 2.5
6 1.74   **7** 0.04   **8** 0.8   **9** 0.107   **10** 40.5
11 3.69   **12** 2.2   **13** 520   **14** 97   **15** 145
16 1860   **17** 703   **18** 6   **19** 0.08   **20** 6.92
21 0.3   **22** 4.8   **23** 1.06   **24** 0.75   **25** 300
26 2080   **27** 4600   **28** 1427   **29** 50   **30** 973
31 0.6   **32** 1.978   **33** 0.25   **34** 0.016   **35** 0.04
36 0.121

C

1 0.03   **2** 2.98   **3** 0.076   **4** 14
5 0.106   **6** 50   **7** 0.6 × 100   **8** 8.2 × 1000
9 0.077 × 10   **10** 1500 ÷ 1000   **11** 4.3 ÷ 100   **12** 0.9 ÷ 10
13 10.83   **14** 61   **15** 0.409   **16** 20
17 0.07   **18** 5

Page 70
A

1 2000 g   **2** 5000 g   **3** 1000 g   **4** 9000 g   **5** 7 kg
6 4 kg   **7** 3 kg   **8** 6 kg   **9** 2500 g   **10** 1250 g
11 500 g   **12** 4250 g   **13** 3.5 kg   **14** 0.25 kg   **15** 2.75 kg
16 1.5 kg   **17** 1.25 kg   **18** 750 g

B

1 1400 g   **2** 7500 g   **3** 200 g   **4** 3600 g   **5** 2.8 kg
6 1.3 kg   **7** 4.5 kg   **8** 0.9 kg   **9** 5700 g   **10** 2300 g
11 1400 g   **12** 100 g   **13** 3.9 kg   **14** 8.8 kg   **15** 0.6 kg
16 4.2 kg   **17** 400 g   **18** 3.6 g

C

1 2370 g   **2** 4630 g   **3** 1280 g   **4** 6050 g   **5** 3.81 kg
6 5.14 kg   **7** 0.52 kg   **8** 9.49 kg   **9** 1280 g   **10** 8540 g
11 3710 g   **12** 650 g   **13** 7.09 kg   **14** 4.32 kg   **15** 2.96 kg
16 5.43 kg   **17** 120 g   **18** 1.8 kg

Page 71
A

1 1.6 kg   **2** 500 g   **3** 82.8 kg   **4** 1.25 kg   **5** 25 g
6 1.4 kg

B

1 300 g   **2** 1.8 kg   **3** 200 g   **4** 2 kg   **5** 350 g   **6** 1.9 kg

C

1 32 g	**2** 1.14 kg	**3** 250 g	**4** 375 g	**5** 1.32 kg
6 120 kg	**7** 120 g			

Page 72

A

1 5005	**2** 7513	**3** 13 392	**4** 3056	**5** 8430
6 78.2	**7** 75.0	**8** 113.7	**9** 127.1	**10** 92.6
11 104 kg	**12** 50.7 kg	**13** £4534		

B

1 41 971	**2** 24 292	**3** 40 136	**4** 30 332	**5** 74 117
6 123.9	**7** 150.59	**8** 106.27	**9** 83.9	**10** 142.35
11 £94.21	**12** 18 118 kg			

C

1 328.47	**2** 83.147	**3** 35.221	**4** 612.258	**5** 53.453
6 19.9	**7** 66.744	**8** 942.26	**9** 22.815	**10** 504.643
11 1.907 kg	**12** 29.135 kg	**13** 2.588 kg		

Page 73

A

1 467	**2** 453	**3** 366	**4** 285	**5** 319
6 51.9	**7** 24.4	**8** 16.0	**9** 45.6	**10** 20.7
11 325 g	**12** 23.7 kg	**13** 38.2 kg		

B

1 2047	**2** 3938	**3** 1613	**4** 6772	**5** 8607
6 10.24	**7** 366.5	**8** 66.16	**9** 57.5	**10** 34.09
11 1177kg	**12** 35.57kg			

C

1 1.482	**2** 45.26	**3** 1.736	**4** 18.21	**5** 2.835
6 4.078	**7** 8.46	**8** 6.168	**9** 0.97	**10** 2.672
11 2.255 kg	**12** 805 g	**13** 271 g		

Page 74

A

1 170	**2** 134	**3** 432	**4** 225	**5** 177
6 325	**7** 178	**8** 372	**9** 288	**10** 228
11 168 g	**12** 138 kg	**13** £1.80		

B

1 1425	**2** 1776	**3** 1114	**4** 2548	**5** 1647
6 4736	**7** 4428	**8** 1424	**9** 55.3	**10** 32.5
11 8.7	**12** 31.2	**13** 27.0	**14** 50.4	**15** 17.8
16 29.6	**17** 55.8	**18** 47.6	**19** 3.4 kg	**20** 17.5 kg

C

1 358.8	**2** 424.8	**3** 115.8	**4** 378.4	**5** 376.6
6 230.4	**7** 189.5	**8** 340.9	**9** 220.8	**10** 235.2
11 186.8 kg	**12** 11 053 kg			

Page 75

A

1 12	**2** 10 r 6	**3** 17	**4** 16 r 3	**5** 19 r 1
6 13	**7** 15 r 3	**8** 12	**9** 28 r 1	**10** 23 r 2
11 35	**12** 26 r 5	**13** 23 r 2	**14** 15 r 3	**15** 16
16 22 r 1	**17** 24 g	**18** 17 kg	**19** 25 kg	

B

1 25 r 3	**2** 36	**3** 41 r 2	**4** 67 r 1	**5** 85
6 59 r 1	**7** 73 r 4	**8** 67 r 4	**9** 118	**10** 51 r 6
11 149 r 1	**12** 96	**13** 140 r 2	**14** 124 r 4	**15** 156
16 73 r 3	**17** 42 g	**18** 34 kg	**19** 34 g	

C

1 197 r 3	**2** 149 r 6	**3** 237	**4** 174 r 2	**5** 168 r 3
6 292	**7** 157 r 6	**8** 169 r 2	**9** 135 r 4	**10** 176
11 337 r 3	**12** 145 r 5	**13** 268 r 3	**14** 173	**15** 269 r 2
16 186 r 7	**17** 435 g	**18** 194 kg		

Page 76

A

1 20 kg, 35 kg	**2** 10 g, 50 g	**3** 50 mm, 90 mm
4 1 m, 5 m	**5** 5 kg, 7.5 kg	**6** 50 g, 100 g
7 640 g, 740 g	**8** 34 cm, 42 cm	**9** 1.25 kg, 2.5 kg
10 500 g, 750 g		

B

1 40 g, 60 g	**2** 8 kg, 10.5 kg	**3** 3.2 kg, 3.9 kg
4 55 g, 80 g	**5** 1.2 kg, 2.8 kg	**6** 40 g, 170 g
7 1.6 kg, 2.7 kg	**8** 67 g, 82 g	**9** 0.25 kg, 0.5 kg
10 125 g, 375 g		

C

1 400 g, 900 g	**2** 0.75 kg, 1.5 kg	**3** 30.5 kg, 34 kg
4 0.03 kg, 0.06 kg	**5** 0.7 kg, 1.6 kg	**6** 0.16 kg, 0.52 kg
7 0.38 kg, 0.46 kg	**8** 0.28 kg, 0.54 kg	**9** 1.3 kg, 2.7 kg
10 125 g, 600 g		

Page 77

A

1 8 cm	**2** 8.6 cm	**3** 8.0 cm	**4** 28 cm	**5** 24 cm
6 18 cm	**7** 20 cm			

B

1 34 cm	**2** 42 cm	**3** 18 cm	**4** 64 cm

5

Length	5 cm	7 cm	8 cm	10 cm	8 cm	9 cm
Width	4 cm	3 cm	5 cm	4 cm	3 cm	7 cm
Perim.	18 cm	20 cm	26 cm	28 cm	22 cm	32 cm

6 28 cm

C

1 22 cm	**2** 36 cm	**3** 54 cm

4

Length	12 cm	4 cm	6 cm	7.5 cm
Width	11 cm	3.5 cm	2.5 cm	5.5 cm
Perim.	46 cm	15 cm	17 cm	26 cm

Page 78

A

1 36 cm²   **2** 35 cm²   **3** 16 cm²   **4** 36 cm²   **5** 20 cm   **6** 24 cm²

B

1

Length	7 cm	8 cm	12 cm	9 cm	8 cm	13 cm
Width	3 cm	5 cm	4 cm	6 cm	4 cm	5 cm
Area	21 cm²	40 cm²	48 cm²	54 cm²	32 cm²	65 cm²

4 2500 m²   **5** 20 cm

C

1 X 40 cm²   Y 120 cm²
3 10 000   **4** 1 000 000
5 £560

2

L cm	W cm	P cm	A cm²
7	5	24	35
12	8	40	96
9	6	30	54
8	6	28	48

Answers

Page 80

A

1 70° **2** 130° **3** 60° **4** 140° **5** 80° **6** 30°
7 125° **8** 95° **9** 60° **10** 30° **11** 100° **12** 170°
13 20° **14** 90° **15** 40° **16** 120° **17** 30° **18** 80°
19 110° **20** 150° **21** 50° **22** 160° **23** 10° **24** 100°
25 CAB, FDE, HIG **26** A acute 40° B obtuse 110°
C obtuse 30° D acute 50° E right ∠ 90°
F acute 40° G obtuse 100°
H acute 35° (allow 30° or 40°) I acute 45° (allow 40° or 50°)

Page 81

B

1 acute **2** obtuse **3** acute **4** obtuse **5** 45° **6** 120°
7 85° **8** 175° **9** 15° **10** 95° **11** 55° **12** 25°
13 20° **14** 75° **15** 110° **16** 155° **17** 35° **18** 165°
19 5° **20** 125° **21** CADB, EFGH **22** A right angle 90°
B obtuse 105° C acute 70° D obtuse 95°
E acute 80° F acute 85° G obtuse 95°
H obtuse 100° **23** (7, 9) **24** (8, 0)

Page 82

C

1 51° **2** 31° **3** 30° **4** 66° **5** 114° **6** 107°
7 168° **8** 138° **9** 93° **10** 54° **11** 7° **12** 92°
13 12° **14** 126° **15** 129° **16** 73° **17** 87° **18** 138°
19 150° **20** 88° **21** 42° **22** 149° **23** 173° **24** 42°
25 A 275° B 308° C 233° D 326° **26** (0, 1) (10, 1) (8, 9)
27 Opposite angles are equal.
The sum of the angles of each quadrilateral equals 360°.
28 The sum of the angles of each triangle equals 180°.

Page 83

A

1 1.4 **2** 1.8 **3** 1.0 **4** 1.6 **5** 1.5 **6** 2.5 **7** 0.5
8 3.5 **9** 2.6 **10** 9.2 **11** 5.8 **12** 1.2 **13** 3.4 **14** 0.8

B

1 0.94 **2** 7.2 **3** 0.18 **4** 11.0 **5** 1.66 **6** 5.4
7 0.76 **8** 3.8 **9** 1.5 **10** 17.6 **11** 0.52 **12** 9.0
13 3.2 **14** 0.14 **15** 0.15 **16** 2.5 **17** 0.28 **18** 3.9
19 0.46 **20** 1.7 **21** 0.36 **22** 0.7 **23** 0.19 **24** 4.8
25 6.1 **26** 0.75 **27** 2.75 **28** 2.05 **29** 4.25 **30** 4.45
31 0.3 **32** 1.07

C

1 0.99 **2** 1.75 **3** 2.62 **4** 0.095 **5** 0.088 **6** 0.66
7 0.146 **8** 4.9 **9** 5.72 **10** 1.34 **11** 3.1 **12** 7.3
13 0.385 **14** 0.824 **15** 1.009 **16** 2.005 **17** 0.36 **18** 3.125
19 0.805 **20** 2.265

Page 84

A

1 $\frac{6}{4}$ $1\frac{2}{4}$, $\frac{7}{4}$ $1\frac{3}{4}$, $\frac{8}{4}$ 2, $\frac{9}{4}$ $2\frac{1}{4}$, $\frac{10}{4}$ $2\frac{2}{4}$
2 $\frac{6}{3}$ 2, $\frac{7}{3}$ $2\frac{1}{3}$, $\frac{8}{3}$ $2\frac{2}{3}$, $\frac{9}{3}$ 3, $\frac{10}{3}$ $3\frac{1}{3}$
3 $\frac{7}{5}$ $1\frac{2}{5}$, $\frac{8}{5}$ $1\frac{3}{5}$, $\frac{9}{5}$ $1\frac{4}{5}$, $\frac{10}{5}$ 2, $\frac{11}{5}$ $2\frac{1}{5}$
4 $\frac{7}{6}$ $1\frac{1}{6}$, $\frac{8}{6}$ $1\frac{2}{6}$, $\frac{9}{6}$ $1\frac{3}{6}$, $\frac{10}{6}$ $1\frac{4}{6}$, $\frac{11}{6}$ $1\frac{5}{6}$
5 $1\frac{1}{3}$ **6** $1\frac{1}{5}$ **7** $2\frac{2}{4}$ or $2\frac{1}{2}$ **8** $1\frac{1}{6}$ **9** $1\frac{4}{5}$
10 $2\frac{1}{3}$ **11** $1\frac{3}{6}$ **12** $1\frac{3}{4}$ **13** $\frac{8}{6}$ **14** $\frac{9}{4}$ **15** $\frac{5}{3}$
16 $\frac{11}{5}$ **17** $\frac{7}{4}$ **18** $\frac{10}{6}$ **19** $\frac{8}{5}$ **20** $\frac{8}{3}$

B

1 $1\frac{2}{3}$ **2** $1\frac{3}{4}$ **3** $\frac{7}{2}$ **4** $\frac{23}{5}$ **5** $6\frac{1}{2}$ **6** $3\frac{1}{6}$
7 $4\frac{2}{5}$ **8** $2\frac{5}{8}$ **9** $6\frac{1}{4}$ **10** $3\frac{2}{7}$ **11** $3\frac{1}{3}$ **12** $1\frac{7}{10}$
13 $\frac{19}{5}$ **14** $\frac{23}{9}$ **15** $\frac{10}{7}$ **16** $\frac{17}{4}$ **17** $\frac{20}{3}$ **18** $\frac{53}{10}$
19 $\frac{15}{8}$ **20** $\frac{14}{6}$ **21** $2\frac{3}{4}$ **22** $4\frac{5}{6}$ **23** $3\frac{1}{5}$ **24** $2\frac{3}{8}$
25 $4\frac{2}{3}$

C

1 $6\frac{1}{4}$ **2** $5\frac{2}{3}$ **3** $4\frac{5}{6}$ **4** $5\frac{2}{7}$ **5** $8\frac{4}{5}$ **6** $6\frac{2}{8}$
7 $6\frac{3}{9}$ **8** $12\frac{3}{10}$ **9** $5\frac{5}{12}$ **10** $2\frac{16}{50}$ **11** $7\frac{12}{100}$ **12** $3\frac{17}{25}$
13 $4\frac{6}{11}$ **14** $3\frac{19}{20}$ **15** $6\frac{4}{15}$ **16** $3\frac{2}{16}$ **17** $\frac{26}{5}$ **18** $\frac{16}{3}$
19 $\frac{27}{4}$ **20** $\frac{57}{6}$ **21** $\frac{20}{7}$ **22** $\frac{57}{8}$ **23** $\frac{129}{10}$ **24** $\frac{47}{12}$
25 $\frac{43}{9}$ **26** $\frac{708}{100}$ **27** $\frac{43}{16}$ **28** $\frac{477}{50}$ **29** $\frac{99}{30}$ **30** $\frac{33}{14}$
31 $\frac{80}{19}$ **32** $\frac{72}{11}$

Page 85

A

1 0.43 **2** 0.7 **3** 0.35 **4** 0.2 **5** 0.5 **6** 0.06
7 0.9 **8** 0.81 **9** $\frac{3}{10}$ **10** $\frac{51}{100}$ **11** $\frac{29}{100}$ **12** $\frac{6}{10}$
13 $\frac{8}{10}$ **14** $\frac{6}{100}$ **15** $\frac{4}{10}$ **16** $\frac{73}{100}$ **17** 2 fifths
18 4 fifths **19** 0.2 **20** 0.6

B

2 $\frac{10}{20} = \frac{1}{2}$ **3** $\frac{18}{20} = \frac{9}{10}$ **4** $0.7 = \frac{14}{20} = \frac{7}{10}$ **5** $0.4 = \frac{8}{20} = \frac{4}{10} = \frac{2}{5}$
6 $\frac{68}{100}$ **7** $\frac{17}{100}$ **8** $\frac{25}{100}$ or $\frac{1}{4}$ **9** $\frac{3}{10}$ **10** $\frac{75}{100}$ or $\frac{3}{4}$
11 $\frac{59}{100}$ **12** $\frac{1}{100}$ **13** $\frac{1}{10}$ **14** 0.5 **15** 0.75
16 0.6 **17** 0.375 **18** 0.25 **19** 0.8 **20** 0.875 **21** 0.95

C

1 0.9 **2** 0.03 **3** 0.3 **4** 0.63 **5** 0.7 **6** 0.78
7 0.344, 0.43, $\frac{3}{4}$ **8** $\frac{19}{100}$, $\frac{9}{10}$, 0.91 **9** $\frac{27}{100}$, 0.5, $\frac{3}{5}$
10 0.188, 0.8, $\frac{81}{100}$ **11** 0.2, $\frac{27}{100}$, $\frac{2}{7}$ **12** 0.556, 0.56, $\frac{5}{6}$
13 0.33 **14** 0.17 **15** 0.08 **16** 0.43 **17** 0.55 **18** 0.56

Page 86

A

1 7 **2** 10 **3** 4 m **4** 10p **5** 3 **6** 10
7 6p **8** 9 cm **9** 5 **10** 9 **11** £10 **12** 8p
13 4 **14** 7 **15** 10 m **16** 5 cm **17** 8 **18** £32
19 14

B

1 12 **2** 28 **3** 54 **4** 24 **5** 24 cm
6 £28 **7** 15kg **8** 9p **9** 8 **10** 1.4 litres
11 120g **12** 15

C

1 350g **2** 40 **3** 24 cm **4** 18 **5** 48
6 69g **7** 350 ml **8** 24 **9** 110 miles **10** 350g
11 1.365 **12** 1.6kg

Page 87

A

1 4 **2** 7 **3** 2 **4** 9 **5** 13 **6** 40
7 25 **8** 100 **9** 2p **10** 8p **11** 30p **12** 24p

13 10p **14** 59p **15** £2.20 **16** £6.00 **17** 5 cm **18** 9 cm
19 10g **20** 60g **21** 10 cm **22** 20 cm **23** 100g **24** 500g
25 £12.60 **26** 77

B

1 (a) 50p   (b) 25p   (c) £1.00   **2** (a) 70 ml
    (b) 35 ml   (c) 140 ml   **3** (a) 200g   (b) 100g
    (c) 400g   **4** (a) 2.5 m   (b) 1.25 m   (c) 5 m
5 £1.80   **6** 90p   **7** 30 cm   **8** 2.7 m
9 40g   **10** 200g   **11** 50 ml   **12** 21 ml
13 £3200   **14** 105   **15** 190

C

1 £3.60   **2** £1.50   **3** 60 cm   **4** 12.5 cm
5 594g   **6** 300g   **7** 30 ml   **8** 9.5 litres
9 40   **10** 140   **11** 80   **12** 20
13 50   **14** 200   **15** 80   **16** 200
17 (a) £2100 (b) £2205

Page 88

A

1 (a) $\frac{27}{100}$ (b) 0.27   (c) 27%

2 (a) $\frac{80}{100}$ or $\frac{8}{10}$ (b) 0.8   (c) 80%

3 (a) $\frac{9}{100}$ (b) 0.09   (c) 9%

4 (a) $\frac{50}{100}$ or $\frac{1}{2}$ (b) 0.5   (c) 50%

5

Fraction	$\frac{1}{2}$	$\frac{1}{10}$	1	$\frac{1}{4}$	$\frac{3}{4}$	$\frac{1}{100}$	$\frac{3}{10}$	$\frac{62}{100}$
Decimal	0.5	0.1	1.0	0.25	0.75	0.01	0.3	0.62
Percentage	50%	10%	100%	25%	75%	1%	30%	62%

6 10%   **7** 75%   **8** 50%
9 1%   **10** 25%

Page 89

B

1 (a) $\frac{1}{2}$ (b) 0.5   (c) 50%

2 (a) $\frac{7}{10}$ (b) 0.7   (c) 70%

3 (a) $\frac{26}{100}$ (b) 0.26   (c) 26%

4 (a) $\frac{65}{100}$ (b) 0.65   (c) 65%

5 (a) $\frac{1}{5}$ (b) 0.2   (c) 20%

6 (a) $\frac{3}{4}$ (b) 0.75   (c) 75%

7 (a) $\frac{72}{100}$ (b) 0.72   (c) 72%

8 (a) $\frac{3}{100}$ (b) 0.03   (c) 3%

9 (a) $\frac{1}{4}$ (b) 0.25   (c) 25%

10 (a) $\frac{2}{5}$ (b) 0.4   (c) 40%

11 (a) $\frac{59}{100}$ (b) 0.59   (c) 59%

12 (a) $\frac{99}{100}$ (b) 0.99   (c) 99%

13 (a) $\frac{1}{10}$ (b) 0.1   (c) 10%

14 (a) $\frac{3}{10}$ (b) 0.3   (c) 30%

15 (a) $\frac{8}{100}$ (b) 0.08   (c) 8%

16 (a) $\frac{80}{100}$ (b) 0.8   (c) 80%

C

1 (a) 0.1   (b) 10%   **2** (a) 0.3   (b) 30%

3 (a) 0.01   (b) 1%   **4** (a) 0.69   (b) 69%
5 (a) 0.07   (b) 7%   **6** (a) 0.2   (b) 20%
7 (a) 0.4   (b) 40%   **8** (a) 0.25   (b) 25%
9 (a) 0.08   (b) 8%   **10** (a) $\frac{1}{2}$ (b) 0.5
11 (a) $\frac{91}{100}$ (b) 0.91   **12** (a) $\frac{2}{25}$ (b) 0.08
13 (a) $\frac{9}{10}$ (b) 0.9   **14** (a) $\frac{4}{5}$ (b) 0.8
15 (a) $\frac{19}{20}$ (b) 0.95   **16** (a) $\frac{3}{4}$ (b) 0.75
17 (a) $\frac{39}{100}$ (b) 0.39   **18** (a) $\frac{4}{25}$ (b) 0.16
19 17%   **20** 35%

21

Subject	Ali	Dan	Mia	Fay
English	61%	39%	58%	47%
Maths	70%	84%	35%	47%
Science	46%	72%	78%	84%
R E	60%	55%	75%	70%
History	80%	76%	64%	52%

22 57%   **23** 25%

Page 90

A

2 (a) 35   (b) 25   (c) 50   **3** (a) 6   (b) 16
4 (a) 5   (b) 10   (c) 30

B

1 18   **2** 6   **3** 32   **4** 15   **5** 12

C

1 25   **2** 81   **3** 30   **4** 75   **5** 15

Page 91

A

1 7.0   **2** 35   **3** 4.0   **4** 21   **5** 1.1
6 25   **7** 7.0   **8** 3.0   **9** 8.0   **10** 5.4

11 0.3 0.5   1.0 1.2   1.5   1.8
0

B

1 5.26, 5.62, 6.25, 6.5, 6.52   **2** 1.38, 1.8, 3.18, 3.8, 3.81
3 6.06, 6.07, 6.6, 6.7, 6.76   **4** 2.08, 2.18, 2.8, 21.8, 28
5 9.5   **6** 4.5   **7** 2.25   **8** 3.15   **9** 1.6
10 1.65   **11** 6.9   **12** 6.25

13 2.91   2.95 2.98 3.0   3.04 3.06
2.9

C

1 0.45, 4.2, 4.25, 4.5, 4.52   **2** 0.67, 6.1, 6.17, 6.7, 6.71
3 0.39, 0.93, 3.09, 3.3, 3.39   **4** 8.22, 8.24, 8.4, 8.42, 8.44
5 2.3   **6** 0.675   **7** 4.357   **8** 1.269   **9** 0.825
10 4.375   **11** 0.985   **12** 7.575

13 2.91 2.925 2.94 2.95   2.975   2.99
2.9

Page 92

A

1 2   **2** 8   **3** 15   **4** 10   **5** 7
6 14   **7** 4   **8** 18   **9** 14   **10** 19
11 £12   **12** £6   **13** £6   **14** £4   **15** £7
16 £9   **17** £5   **18** £3   **19** £5   **20** £10

Answers

B

1 £9	**2** £27	**3** £4	**4** £6	**5** £13
6 £8	**7** £4	**8** £10	**9** £15	**10** £7
11 5	**12** 6	**13** 4	**14** 12	**15** 8
16 13	**17** 1	**18** 5	**19** 28	**20** 13
21 6 m	**22** 4 m	**23** 10 m	**24** 6 m	**25** 3 m
26 1 m	**27** 8 m	**28** 12 m	**29** 8 m	**30** 5 m
31 4 kg	**32** 4 kg	**33** 12 kg	**34** 9 kg	**35** 5 kg
36 4 kg	**37** 16 kg	**38** 8 kg	**39** 12 kg	**40** 9 kg

C

1 £1.30	**2** £5.80	**3** £9.60	**4** £31.40	**5** £7.50
6 £4.50	**7** £0.10	**8** £2.70	**9** £8.20	**10** £7.00
11 2.6	**12** 3.3	**13** 14.1	**14** 0.7	**15** 5.6
16 8.5	**17** 30.0	**18** 1.4	**19** 52.1	**20** 6.8
21 4.2 m	**22** 1.6 m	**23** 7.5 m	**24** 2.8 m	**25** 0.5 m
26 3.4 m	**27** 5.9 m	**28** 12.1 m	**29** 0.3 m	**30** 8.8 m
31 6.5 litres	**32** 9.1 litres	**33** 18.9 litres	**34** 35.2 litres	**35** 20.3 litres

Page 93

A

1 0.5, 1.0, 1.5, 2.0   **2** 0.2, 0.4, 0.6, 0.8, 1.0, 1.2
3 0.3, 0.6, 0.9, 1.2, 1.5, 1.8, 2.1   **4** 0.9, 1.8, 2.7, 3.6
5 0.6, 1.2, 1.8, 2.4, 3.0   **6** 3.2, 2.4, 1.6, 0.8, 0
7 2.4, 2.0, 1.6, 1.2, 0.8, 0.4, 0   **8** 3.5, 2.8, 2.1, 1.4, 0.7, 0
9 3.5, 3.0, 2.5, 2.0, 1.5, 1.0, 0.5, 0
10 1.8, 1.6, 1.4, 1.2, 1.0, 0.8, 0.6, 0.4, 0.2, 0
11 1.8, 1.5, 1.2, 0.9, 0.6, 0.3, 0

B

1 3.6, 4.2, 4.8, 5.4, 6.0, 6.6   **2** 8.1, 7.2, 6.3, 5.4, 4.5, 3.6
3 0.02, 0.04, 0.06, 0.08, 0.1, 0.12   **4** 0.15, 0.12, 0.09, 0.06, 0.03, 0
5 0.05, 0.1, 0.15, 0.2, 0.25, 0.3   **6** 1.2   **7** 4.5
8 4.8   **9** 2.7   **10** 5.6   **11** 8   **12** 9
13 5   **14** 7   **15** 6

C

1 1.25, 2.0, 2.75, 3.5, 4.25, 5.0
2 0.3, 0.45, 0.6, 0.75, 0.9, 1.05
3 1.91, 1.93, 1.95, 1.97, 1.99, 2.01
4 0.05, 0.075, 0.1, 0.125, 0.15, 0.175
5 0.45, 1.1, 1.75, 2.4, 3.05, 3.7
6 0.07×3 **7** 0.05×4 **8** 0.09×6 **9** 0.008×9
10 0.007×6 **11** $0.72 \div 8$ **12** $0.49 \div 7$ **13** $0.4 \div 8$
14 $0.03 \div 6$ **15** $0.027 \div 3$

Page 94

A

1 £33.60   **2** 1.2 m   **3** 56.3 litres   **4** 3.2g   **5** £5.30   **6** 26

B

1 36   **2** −52.1°C   **3** £5.52   **4** 22.8 m   **5** 3.75 litres

C

1 £1.35   **2** £2830.50   **3** 54.4 m   **4** 0.48 g   **5** 415 ml   **6** 7

Page 95

A

1 360	**2** 828	**3** 752	**4** 696	**5** 450
6 918	**7** 988	**8** 836		

B

1 476	**2** 928	**3** 1564	**4** 560	**5** 667
6 1222	**7** 1330			

C

1 722	**2** 1484	**3** 1105	**4** 2160	**5** 2412
6 3888	**7** 1677	**8** 3016	**9** 2232	**10** 2665
11 2072	**12** 4662	**13** 3010	**14** 3942	**15** 9485
16 7728	**17** 8195	**18** 15 283	**19** 6624	**20** 17712

Page 96

A

1 1390	**2** 3168	**3** 24.5	**4** 20.7	**5** 296
6 1404	**7** 22.8	**8** 23.4		

B

1 498	**2** 1492	**3** 1295	**4** 1068	**5** 8.4
6 85.5	**7** 13.4	**8** 35.4	**9** 2142	**10** 2345
11 1544	**12** 1650	**13** 24.0	**14** 60.8	**15** 35.6
16 50.4	**17** 52.2 litres	**18** 57.6 kg		

C

1 10 832	**2** 24 921	**3** 27 426	**4** 17 068	**5** 213.3
6 303.6	**7** 116.8	**8** 229.2	**9** 4.77	**10** 19.11
11 32.4	**12** 31.36	**13** 25.28 m	**14** 13.65 litres	**15** 8.9 km

Page 97

A

1 18	**2** 17	**3** 12 r 2	**4** 17 r 4	**5** 23 r 1
6 14 r 2	**7** 17 r 2	**8** 15 r 1	**9** 13 r 3	**10** 19
11 12 r 2	**12** 18 r 3	**13** 13 r 4	**14** 17 r 2	**15** 17 r 7
16 16 r 1	**17** 84	**18** £26		

B

1 21 r 2	**2** 15 r 3	**3** 22 r 5	**4** 21 r 5	**5** 14 r 3
6 28 r 2	**7** 27 r 5	**8** 29 r 2	**9** 37 r 5	**10** 32 r 6
11 43 r 1	**12** 35 r 1	**13** 41 r 6	**14** 31 r 6	**15** 38 r 8
16 66 r 3	**17** 23	**18** 26	**19** 144	

C

1 62 r 4	**2** 45	**3** 73 r 3	**4** 57	**5** 96 r 1
6 64 r 5	**7** 81 r 2	**8** 78	**9** 12 r 4	**10** 23
11 15	**12** 24	**13** 11 r 8	**14** 26	**15** 12 r 16
16 23 r 18	**17** 23g	**18** 29	**19** 24	**20** 25

Page 98

A

2 4.8 + 5.2   **3** 14   **4** 300   **5** 17 cm   **6** 15 cm
7 58 + 27   **8** 43 − 25

9
$$\begin{array}{r} 67 \\ \times\, 2 \\ \hline 134 \end{array}$$

10
$$\begin{array}{r} 86 \\ \times\, 4 \\ \hline 344 \end{array}$$

B

3 10 = 8.37 + 1.63   **4** 10 = 6.51 + 3.49   **5** 37   **6** 188
7 43 cm   **8** (a) 26, 27   (b) 14, 15   **9** (a) 14, 16
(b) 13, 19   **10** (a) 25, 28   (b) 21, 22

C

3 4.25×8 or 8.25×4 **4** 46 cm   **5** 4.94   **6** 0.9
7 26   **8** 1.9   **9** 126   **10** 61.1   **11** 173.6
12 18.24   **13** 48, 49   **14** 33, 38

Page 99

A

2

Pattern	1	2	3	4	5
Matches	3	6	9	12	15

3 …three times…   **4** (a) 18   (b) 30   (c) 60
(d) 300

B

2

Pattern	1	2	3	4	5
Dots	4	6	8	10	12

3 ... two times the number of the pattern plus two.
4 (a) 20 (b) 30 (c) 74 **5** (a) 7th (b) 11th (c) 19th

C

1 (a) 15 (b) 33 (c) 79 **2** (a) 13th (b) 26th (c) 107th
3 (a) 29 (b) 93 (c) 397 **4** (a) 6th (b) 17th (c) 33rd
5 (a) Double the number of the pattern plus one.
　 (b) Four times the number of the pattern take three.

Page 100
A

1 8 and 3 **2** 3 and 5 **3** 6 and 7 **4** 9 and 2 **5** 7 and 4
6 5 and 8 **7** 9 and 6 **8** 8 and 9 **9** 1, 2, 5, 10
10 1, 2, 7, 14 **11** 1, 2, 4, 5, 10, 20 **12** 1, 2, 3, 4, 6, 8, 12, 24
13 1, 3, 9, 27 **14** 1, 2, 4, 8, 16 **15** 1, 2, 3, 5, 6, 10, 15, 30
16 1, 2, 3, 6, 7, 14, 21, 42 **17** 36, 40, 24 **18** 36, 24, 25
19 36, 40, 24 **20** 40, 45

B

1 1, 2, 3, 4, 6, 9, 12, 18, 36 **2** 1, 2, 4, 11, 22, 44
3 1, 3, 17, 51 **4** 1, 5, 13, 65
5 1, 3, 9, 11, 33, 99 **6** 1, 3, 5, 15, 25, 75
7 1, 2, 3, 4, 6, 8, 12, 16, 24, 48
8 1, 2, 3, 5, 6, 9, 10, 15, 18, 30, 45, 90
9 (a) Laila is right.
　 (b) Square numbers have an odd number of factors.
10 36 **11** 6, 12, 18, 24, 30, etc. They are all multiples of 6.

C

1 1, 7, 49 **2** 1, 2, 3, 4, 5, 6, 10, 12, 15, 20, 30, 60
3 1, 3, 19, 57 **4** 1, 2, 4, 17, 34, 68
5 1, 2, 4, 23, 46, 92 **6** 1, 2, 3, 4, 6, 8, 9, 12, 18, 24, 36, 72
7 1, 2, 7, 14, 49, 98 **8** 1, 2, 4, 5, 10, 20, 25, 50, 100
9 24 and 54 **10** 90 **11** 12 **12** 19 **13** 16
14 15 **15** They are multiples of 15. **16** They are multiples of 20.

Page 101
A

1 3, 6, 9, 12, 15, 18 **2** 8, 16, 24, 32, 40, 48
3 11, 22, 33, 44, 55, 66 **4** 7, 14, 21, 28, 35, 42
5 4, 8, 12, 16, 20, 24 **6** 9, 18, 27, 36, 45, 54
7 25 **8** 54 **9** 205 **10** 60 **11** Yes **12** No
13 Yes **14** No **15** Yes **16** No **17** Yes **18** No

B

1 True **2** True **3** False **4** True **5** True **6** False
7 True **8** False **9** True **10** False **11** True **12** True
13 Dani's statement is true.

C

3 e.g. 100, 200, 300, etc. are divisible by 4. 52 is a multiple of 4.
　 Therefore, so is 152, 252, 352, etc.
5 24, 27, 36, 42, 45, 54, 57, 63, 72, 75
6 24, 32, 36, 52, 56, 64, 72, 76

Page 102
A

1 1.7 + 2.7 **2** 0.7 × 5 **3** 6.7 **4** 3.6
5 3 × 8 8 × 3 4 × 6 6 × 4
6 0.3 + 3.7 1.3 + 2.7 2.3 + 1.7 3.3 + 0.7

7 6 **8** 7.6 + 6.9 **9** 15.4 + 5.9 **10** 22.4 – 13.7
11 22.6 – 9.4 **12** (a) 19, 20 (b) 13, 14

B

1 6.1 – 0.85 **2** 16.8 ÷ 7 **3** 5.05 **4** 5.07
5 0.4 × 5 0.5 × 4 **6** 60 ÷ 10 = 6 60 ÷ 12 = 5 60 ÷ 15 = 4
7 2.5 **8** 43 × 26 **9** 1890 ÷ 35 = 54
10 (2.9 × 3) + 0.6 **11** (496 ÷ 8) – 25 **12** (a) 76, 77 (b) 54, 55

C

1 3.792 + 1.308 **2** 2.35 × 4 **3** 1.98 **4** 2.835
5 100 ÷ 20 = 5.0 100 ÷ 25 = 4.0 100 ÷ 40 = 2.5 100 ÷ 50 = 2.0
6 0.5 × 6 0.6 × 5 1.0 × 3 1.5 × 2 **7** 4.3
8 0.82 + (3.56 ÷ 4) **9** (56.7 ÷ 9) × 4.8 **10** 87 × 39
11 2812 ÷ 76 = 37 **12** (a) 13, 17 (b) 19, 23

Page 103
A

1 18 **2** 30p **3** 84 **4** 18 **5** 120

B

1 1440 **2** 125 **3** 80 **4** 2851 miles **5** £3.68 **6** 45g

C

1 50 **2** 268 **3** 7 **4** £7481 **5** £2.24 **6** 1536

Page 104
A

1 All angles are 60° **2** 90°

B

1 All angles are 120°. **2** All angles are 108°.
4 Opposite angles are equal.

C

1

Sides	3	4	5	6	7
Angle	60°	90°	108°	120°	128.6°
Sum of Angles	180°	360°	540°	720°	900°

2

Sides	8	9	10
Angle	135°	140°	144°
Sum of Angles	1080°	1260°	1440°

4 A symmetrical trapezium has 2 pairs of equal adjacent angles.

Page 106
A

1 D **2** C **3** F **4** E **5** A **6** B

Page 107
B

1 (a) 140 bpm (b) 145 bpm **2** (a) 11:10 (b) 11:40
3 11:35 **4** 150 bpm **5** 80 bpm
7 Between 06:00 and 08:00. Heating switched on.

C

1 (a) 19°C (b) October (c) April, November
　 (d) September, October (e) 21°C (–3°C to 18°C) (f) 5
2 (a) Week 9 (b) Week 8

Page 108
A

1 5 cm **2** 2 cm **3** 30 mm **4** 60 mm **5** 8 m

6 1 m   **7** 900 cm   **8** 400 cm   **9** 2 km   **10** 7 km
11 6000 m   **12** 3000 m   **13** km   **14** mm   **15** km
16 mm   **17** cm   **18** mm

B

1 2.1 cm   **2** 7.2 cm   **3** 18 mm   **4** 6 mm   **5** 5.1 m
6 8.7 m   **7** 310 cm   **8** 930 cm   **9** 6.5 km   **10** 2.9 km
11 4400 m   **12** 200 m   **13** km   **14** km   **15** m
16 mm   **17** cm   **18** mm

C

1 4.34 m   **2** 7.99 m   **3** 0.21 m   **4** 252 cm   **5** 107 cm
6 583 cm   **7** 0.45 km   **8** 3.18 km   **9** 4.62 km   **10** 1240 m
11 60 m   **12** 1730 m   **13** 140 mm   **14** 42000 m   **15** 0.3 m
16 0.4 km   **17** 0.12 m

Page 109

A

1 (a) 12m   (b) 28 m   **2** (a) Thursday   (b) Monday
3 3 m   **4** 3 m   **5** (a) Friday   (b) Wednesday
6 (a) Thursday   (b) Thursday

B

1 (a) Stu   (b) Jake   (c) Amit   (d) Naomi, Zena
2 (a) 8 m   (b) 7 m   (c) 6 m   **3** (a) Stu   (b) Carol, Jake
4

Name	Amit	Carol	Jake	Naomi	Stu	Zena
Improvement	9 m	6 m	6 m	8 m	11 m	10 m

C

1

Name	Amit	Carol	Jake	Naomi	Stu	Zena
Percentage Improvement	75%	60%	25%	50%	55%	40%

Page 110

B

5 Expected frequencies should be:
     1   15
     2   10
     3   5

C

1 $\frac{1}{5}$ **2** $\frac{5}{6}$ **3** $\frac{2}{7}$ **4** $\frac{4}{8}$ or $\frac{1}{2}$ **5** $\frac{3}{5}$
6 $\frac{2}{6}$ or $\frac{1}{3}$ **7** $\frac{4}{7}$ **8** $\frac{1}{8}$

Page 111

A

1 50 ml, 75 ml   **2** 0.25 litres, 0.5 litres   **3** 400 ml, 900 ml
4 10 ml, 70 ml   **5** 0.6 litres, 1.3 litres   **6** 20 ml, 170 ml
7 0.5 litres, 1 litre   **8** 250 ml, 750 ml

B

1 50 ml, 125 ml   **2** 0.125 litres, 0.75 litres
3 0.8 litres, 1.4 litres   **4** 15 ml, 40 ml
5 0.35 litres, 0.9 litres   **6** 80 ml, 260 ml
7 0.25 litres, 0.5 litres   **8** 125 ml, 375 ml

C

1 125 ml, 875 ml   **2** 0.75 litres, 1.25 litres
3 150 ml, 300 ml   **4** 0.8 litres, 1.6 litres
5 0.24 litres, 0.68 litres   **6** 75 ml, 300 ml
7 0.375 litres, 0.6 litres   **8** 250 ml, 1700 ml

Page 112

A

1 7   **2** 15   **3** 7   **4** 6   **5** 17

B

1 13   **2** 25   **3** 33   **4** 23   **5** 16   **6** 29

C

1 34   **2** 12   **3** 13   **4** 167   **5** 15   **6** 31

Page 113

A

1 750 ml   **2** 300 ml   **3** 400 ml   **4** 1.7 litres   **5** 3 litres
6 160 ml   **7** 3 litres

B

1 1.15 litres   **2** 1.8 litres   **3** 12.8 litres   **4** 3.5 litres   **5** 25 days
6 80

C

1 200 ml   **2** 400 ml   **3** 3.6 litres   **4** 11.7 litres   **5** 40
6 21 litres   **7** 1.475 litres

Page 114

A

1 (a) 25 mins.   (b) 45 mins.   (c) 1 h. 6 mins.   **2** 7
3 09:54   **4** 11:35   **5** 15 mins.   **6** 12:52

B

1 (a) 1h. 42 mins.   (b) 2h. 32 mins.   (c) 3h. 43 mins.
2 2   **3** 14:07   **4** 09:21   **5** 27 mins.   **6** 12:01

C

1 (a) 41 mins.   (b) 1h. 29 mins.   (c) 2h. 32 mins.
2 2   **3** 16:34   **4** 13:17   **5** 53 mins.   **6** 15:31

Page 115

A

1 a 30°   **2** b 70°   **3** c 100°   **4** d 120°   **5** e 115°
6 f 55°   **7** g 125°   **8** h 85°

B

1 i 105°   **2** j 44°   **3** k 132°   **4** l 38°   **5** m 121°
6 n 26°   **7** o 143°   **8** p 67°

C

1 q 40°   **2** r 53°   **3** s 46°   **4** t 47°   **5** u 287°
6 v 213°   **7** w 112°   **8** x 104°

Page 116

A

1 J 70°,   K 50°,   L 60°   **4** 40°

B

2 M 105°,   N 75°,   O 95°,   P 85°
3 (a) acute   (b) obtuse   (c) acute   (d) obtuse   (e) acute
     (f) obtuse   **4** 125°

C

1 (a) S 73°,   R 17°,   T 90°   (b) Q 56°,   T 51°,   R 73°
     (c) Q 39°,   T 39°,   U 102°   (d) R 90°,   S 73°,   U 102°,   Q 95°
3 The sum of the angles of each triangle equals 180°.

Page 117

A

1 (a) 8 cm   (b) 4 cm²   **2** (a) 18 cm   (b) 20 cm²
3 (a) 24 cm   (b) 36 cm²   **4** (a) 20 cm   (b) 16 cm²
7 9 cm²

B

L	7	10	8	9	15	6
W	2	3	6	3	4	3
P	18	26	28	24	38	18
A	14	30	48	27	60	18

4 (a) (4, 6)   (b) 12 cm   (c) 8 cm²
5 (a) (4, 1)   (b) 16 cm   (c) 15 cm²

C

1 Shape 1   (a) 52 cm   (b) 112 cm²
  Shape 2   (a) 120 cm   (b) 336 cm²
3 (a) 60 cm   (b) 225 cm²
4 (a) (6, 5)   (b) 14 cm² approx.   (c) 12 cm² approx.
5 (a) (1, 0)   (b) 19 cm² approx.   (c) 20 cm² approx.

Page 118

B

Allow +/– 0.1 cm
1 9.9 cm   **2** 7.8 cm   **3** 5 cm   **4** allow 9.8 cm or 9.9 cm
5 6.4 cm   **6** 6.5 cm

C

1 9 cm   **2** 4.0 cm (allow 3.9 cm)   **3** 9.1 cm   **4** 7.1 cm
5 (a) allow 6.3 cm or 6.4 cm   (b) allow 5.2 cm or 5.3 cm

Page 120

B

1 (b) (0, 4) (0, 6) (3, 4)   (c) (3, 3) (3, 1) (6, 1)
2 (a) (2, 1) (4, 2) (4, 3) (2, 3)   (b) (0, 4) (2, 5) (2, 6) (0, 6)

C

1 (b) (1, 0) (2, 2) (3, 1)   (c) (4, 2) (5, 4) (6, 3)
2 (a) (2, 5) (3, 6) (5, 4) (4, 3)   (b) (0, 3) (1, 4) (3, 2) (2, 1)

Page 121

A

1 Red   0 5 10 15 20 25 30 35 40 45 50
   Yellow 0 3 6 9 12 15 18 21 24 27 30
2 (a) 20   (b) 35   (c) 40   **3** (a) 15   (b) 27
4 (a) 18   (b) 30   (c) 21

B

1 (a) 100 g flour   (b) 400 g flour
    20 g cheese   80 g cheese
    60 g butter   240 g butter
 2 28   **3** 36   **4** 16

C

1 (a) 1 banana   (b) 3 bananas
    125 ml ice cream   375 ml ice cream
    50 ml cream   150 ml cream
    15 ml honey   45 ml honey
 (c) 10 bananas   1.25 litres ice cream
    500 ml cream   150 ml honey
2 36   **3** 280   **4** 50

Page 122

A

1 7   **2** 9   **3** 4   **4** 8   **5** 7 p   **6** £1.40
7 10 cm   **8** 25g   **9** 32   **10** 2750   **11** £3.60   **12** 44kg

B

1 14   **2** 60   **3** 30   **4** 16   **5** 18p
6 24p   **7** 600 ml   **8** 18 cm   **9** 288 mm   **10** 18
11 £208

C

1 42   **2** 40   **3** 52   **4** 520   **5** 75p   **6** £5.40
7 390g   **8** 760 ml   **9** 57   **10** 900g   **11** 128

Page 123

A

1 $\frac{1}{2}=\frac{5}{10}$ **2** $\frac{3}{4}=\frac{6}{8}$ **3** $\frac{1}{2}=\frac{3}{6}$ **4** $\frac{3}{10}=\frac{30}{100}$
5 $\frac{2}{3}=\frac{4}{6}$ **6** $\frac{3}{5}=\frac{6}{10}$ **7** $\frac{3}{4}=\frac{9}{12}$ **8** $\frac{1}{4}=\frac{25}{100}$

B

1 $\frac{4}{8}$ **2** $\frac{2}{6}$ **3** $\frac{6}{10}$ **4** $\frac{10}{12}$ **5** $\frac{2}{8}$
6 $\frac{9}{12}$ **7** $\frac{2}{3}$ **8** $\frac{1}{6}$ **9** $\frac{3}{4}$ **10** $\frac{4}{8}$
11 $\frac{3}{4}=\frac{6}{8}=\frac{9}{12}=\frac{12}{16}$ **12** $\frac{1}{6}=\frac{2}{12}=\frac{3}{18}=\frac{4}{24}$
13 $\frac{2}{5}=\frac{4}{10}=\frac{6}{15}=\frac{8}{20}$ **14** $\frac{1}{8}=\frac{2}{16}=\frac{3}{24}=\frac{4}{32}$

C

1 $\frac{6}{9}$ **2** $\frac{5}{20}$ **3** $\frac{7}{14}$ **4** $\frac{6}{18}$ **5** $\frac{20}{25}$
6 $\frac{90}{100}$ **7** $\frac{20}{100}$ **8** $\frac{10}{15}$ **9** $\frac{12}{30}$ **10** $\frac{15}{60}$
11 $\frac{3}{4}$ **12** $\frac{2}{5}$ **13** $\frac{4}{10}$ **14** $\frac{5}{6}$ **15** $\frac{3}{5}$
16 $\frac{4}{7}$ **17** $\frac{4}{9}$ **18** $\frac{2}{3}$ **19** $\frac{8}{20}$ **20** $\frac{5}{8}$
21 $\frac{10}{26},\frac{15}{39},\frac{20}{52}$, etc.   **22** $\frac{2}{9},\frac{4}{18},\frac{6}{27}$, etc.
23 $\frac{1}{4},\frac{2}{8},\frac{3}{12}$, etc.   **24** $\frac{6}{11},\frac{12}{22},\frac{24}{44}$, etc.
25 $\frac{18}{32},\frac{27}{48},\frac{36}{64}$, etc.   **26** $\frac{7}{8},\frac{14}{16},\frac{21}{24}$, etc.
27 $\frac{2}{5},\frac{4}{10},\frac{6}{15}$, etc.   **28** $\frac{8}{25},\frac{16}{50},\frac{24}{75}$, etc.

Page 124

A

1 $\frac{1}{4}$ **2** $\frac{1}{8}$ **3** $\frac{1}{6}$ **4** $\frac{1}{10}$ **5** $\frac{1}{2}$ **6** $\frac{1}{6}$
7 $\frac{2}{7}$ **8** $\frac{3}{4}$ **9** $\frac{1}{2}$ **10** $\frac{5}{8}$ **11** $\frac{1}{3}$ **12** $\frac{9}{10}$
13 $\frac{4}{8},\frac{5}{10},\frac{3}{6}$ **14** $\frac{2}{6},\frac{4}{10},\frac{3}{8},\frac{1}{4}$ **15** $\frac{2}{3},\frac{3}{4},\frac{3}{5}$

B

1 $\frac{1}{5}$ **2** $\frac{1}{3}$ **3** $\frac{3}{8}$ **4** $\frac{4}{10}$ or $\frac{2}{5}$ **5** $\frac{3}{10}$
6 $\frac{3}{8}$ **7** $1\frac{1}{6}$ **8** $\frac{1}{10}$ **9** $1\frac{1}{6}$ **10** $\frac{2}{5}$ or $\frac{4}{10}$
11 $\frac{1}{4},\frac{3}{8},\frac{1}{2},\frac{3}{4}$ **12** $\frac{2}{6},\frac{1}{2},\frac{2}{3},\frac{5}{6}$ **13** $\frac{1}{5},\frac{4}{10},\frac{1}{2},\frac{3}{5}$
14 $\frac{1}{2},\frac{3}{4},1\frac{1}{8},1\frac{1}{4}$ **15** $\frac{2}{3},\frac{5}{6},1\frac{1}{3},1\frac{1}{2}$ **16** $\frac{1}{2},\frac{7}{10},1\frac{3}{10},1\frac{2}{5}$
17 $\frac{50}{100},\frac{10}{20},\frac{25}{50}$ **18** $\frac{5}{12},\frac{12}{25},\frac{45}{100},\frac{4}{9}$ **19** $\frac{4}{7},\frac{6}{11},\frac{9}{16}$

C

1 $\frac{3}{16}$ **2** $\frac{7}{20}$ **3** $\frac{5}{12}$ **4** $\frac{1}{24}$ **5** $\frac{9}{20}$
6 $\frac{1}{12}$ **7** $\frac{7}{16}$ **8** $\frac{33}{100}$ **9** $\frac{1}{2},\frac{9}{16},\frac{5}{8},\frac{3}{4}$

10 $\frac{4}{9}, \frac{7}{12}, \frac{2}{3}, \frac{5}{6}$ **11** $\frac{48}{100}, 1\frac{2}{5}, 1\frac{9}{20}, 1\frac{6}{10}$ **12** $\frac{4}{6}, \frac{3}{4}, 1\frac{5}{12}, 1\frac{1}{2}$

13 $\frac{3}{4}$ **14** $\frac{1}{2}$ **15** $\frac{7}{10}$ **16** $\frac{3}{8}$ **17** $\frac{3}{12}$ or $\frac{1}{4}$

18 $\frac{13}{20}$ **19** $\frac{7}{16}$ **20** $\frac{17}{24}$ **21** $\frac{17}{40}$ **22** $\frac{7}{24}$

Page 125

A

1 3×4 **2** $\frac{1}{3}$ of 12 **3** 2×5 **4** $\frac{1}{2}$ of 10 **5** 3×8

6 $\frac{1}{3}$ of 24 **7** $\frac{2}{3}$ of 24 **8** 7×4 **9** $\frac{1}{7}$ of 28 **10** $\frac{2}{7}$ of 28

B

1 (a) $\frac{1}{8}$ (b) $\frac{1}{4}$ (c) $\frac{1}{2}$ (d) $\frac{1}{16}$

2 (a) $\frac{1}{12}$ (b) $\frac{1}{4}$ (c) $\frac{1}{6}$ (d) $\frac{1}{2}$

3 (a) $\frac{1}{2}$ (b) $\frac{3}{10}$ (c) $\frac{1}{100}$ (d) $\frac{1}{4}$

4 (a) $\frac{6}{10}$ or $\frac{3}{5}$ (b) $\frac{3}{4}$ (c) $\frac{1}{20}$ (d) $\frac{1}{100}$

5 $\frac{4}{5}$ **6** $\frac{1}{3}$ **7** $\frac{1}{4}$

C

1 (a) $\frac{1}{4}$ (b) $\frac{3}{4}$ (c) $\frac{1}{8}$ (d) $\frac{3}{8}$

2 (a) $\frac{1}{4}$ (b) $\frac{3}{4}$ (c) $\frac{1}{8}$ (d) $\frac{5}{8}$

3 (a) $\frac{1}{500}$ (b) $\frac{9}{10}$ (c) $\frac{2}{5}$ (d) $\frac{1}{100}$

4 (a) $\frac{1}{20}$ (b) $\frac{1}{4}$ (c) $\frac{5}{8}$ (d) $\frac{1}{2000}$

5 $\frac{5}{12}$ **6** $\frac{2}{5}$ **7** $\frac{1}{25}$

Page 126

A

1 True **2** False **3** False **4** True **5** False **6** False
7 True **8** False **9** True **10** True **11** True **12** False

13 $\frac{1}{2} = 50\%$ $\frac{4}{10} = 0.4$ $\frac{5}{100} = 5\%$
$\frac{2}{10} = 20\%$ $\frac{14}{100} = 0.14$ $\frac{1}{4} = 0.25$

B

1 $\frac{68}{100}$ **2** $\frac{1}{2}$ **3** $\frac{17}{100}$ **4** $\frac{3}{10}$ **5** $\frac{3}{4}$
6 $\frac{59}{100}$ **7** $\frac{9}{100}$ **8** $\frac{9}{10}$ **9** 0.46 **10** 0.25
11 0.04 **12** 0.4 **13** 0.18 **14** 0.08 **15** 0.01
16 0.8 **17** 20% **18** 25% **19** 2% **20** 24%
21 30% **22** 3% **23** 50% **24** 35% **25** 0.9
26 0.03 **27** 0.3 **28** 0.63 **29** 70% **30** 88%
31 64% **32** 43%

C

1 0.344, 43%, $\frac{3}{4}$ **2** 19%, $\frac{9}{10}$, 0.91

3 35%, 0.5, $\frac{3}{5}$ **4** 8%, 0.188, $\frac{81}{100}$

5 0.2, 27%, $\frac{2}{7}$ **6** 0.556, 56%, $\frac{5}{6}$

7 30%, 0.311, $\frac{1}{3}$ **8** 0.1, $\frac{101}{1000}$, 11%

9 80% **10** 29% **11** 81% **12** 19% **13** 0.42
14 0.13 **15** 0.25 **16** 0.15 **17** 0.35 kg

Page 127

A

1 24 **2** 16 **3** 17 **4** 17 **5** 12 r 2

6 19 **7** 17 r 2 **8** 14 **9** 14 r 2 **10** 14
11 15 r 2 **12** 14 **13** 16 r 2 **14** 13 r 1 **15** 19
16 17 **17** 13 **18** £16 **19** 19 **20** £14.50

B

1 23 **2** 44 r 6 **3** 31 r 2 **4** 47 **5** 57 r 5
6 26 r 1 **7** 28 **8** 31 r 8 **9** 25 r 1 **10** 38 r 3
11 47 r 1 **12** 38 r 6 **13** 48 r 2 **14** 38 r 6 **15** 38 r 6
16 46 r 6 **17** 210 **18** 67g

C

1 73 **2** 45 r 2 **3** 57 r 4 **4** 62 **5** 56 r 7
6 78 r 3 **7** 63 r 5 **8** 57 r 2 **9** 12 **10** 14
11 21 r 6 **12** 22 r 20 **13** 32 r 2 **14** 21 r 4 **15** 34 r 12
16 22 r 30 **17** 19, 6 left over **18** 26 **19** 35g

Page 128

A

1 17 **2** 13 **3** 7 **4** 17 **5** 22 **6** 3

B

1 17 **2** 37 **3** 34 **4** 21 **5** 17 **6** 13

C

1 63 **2** 58 **3** 16 **4** 15 **5** 14 **6** 26
7 24

Page 129

A

1 $16\frac{1}{2}$ **2** $14\frac{3}{5}$ **3** $6\frac{1}{3}$ **4** $13\frac{7}{10}$ **5** $6\frac{3}{4}$
6 $10\frac{1}{2}$ **7** $6\frac{3}{5}$ **8** $9\frac{1}{4}$ **9** $7\frac{2}{3}$ **10** $12\frac{2}{5}$
11 £8.50 **12** £7.70 **13** £7.25 **14** £5.60 **15** £5.75
16 £13.50 **17** £4.75 **18** £11.40 **19** £1.20 **20** £7.80
21 15.5m **22** £3.40 **23** £11.50

B

1 $20\frac{3}{4}$ **2** $5\frac{4}{7}$ **3** $8\frac{1}{9}$ **4** $6\frac{2}{6}$

5 $5\frac{11}{25}$ **6** $21\frac{4}{5}$ **7** $5\frac{3}{8}$ **8** $17\frac{3}{10}$

9 $6\frac{41}{100}$ **10** $3\frac{5}{7}$ **11** 23.5 **12** 31.75

13 26.2 **14** 42.7 **15** 23.25 **16** £1.60
17 £2.30 **18** £2.40 **19** £4.55 **20** £1.35
21 £68.40 **22** 28.75 litres

C

1 86 **2** 39 **3** 73 **4** 95 **5** 1491
6 157 **7** 167 **8** 172 **9** 23.5 **10** 13.7
11 18.8 **12** 12.9 **13** 17.3 **14** 12.3 **15** 15.8
16 14.5 **17** 31.25 km **18** 0.625kg

Page 130

1 seventy-five thousand two hundred and forty
2 three hundred and twenty thousand one hundred and eight
3 one million four hundred and seven thousand eight hundred and fifty
4 two million ninety thousand and sixteen
5 9000 **6** 500 000 **7** 40 000 **8** 3 000 000 **9** 2490
10 30 000 **11** 41 800 **12** 3700 **13** 150 000 **14** 46 100
15 4200 **16** 30 000 **17** 602 **18** 230 **19** 586
20 2000 **21** 9652 **22** 2569 **23** 900 **24** 1200
25 3000 **26** 4700 **27** 7000 **28** 15 000 **29** 26 000
30 20 000 **31** 550 **32** 780 **33** 50 **34** 70
35 200 **36** 350 **37** (a) −16 (b) −2 (c) 6
(d) 14 **38** 14 **39** 8 **40** 22

41 16　　**42** –6, –3, –2, 0, 1, 5　　**43** 21, 36, 45, 60
44 28, 36, 56, 60　　**45** 21, 28, 56　　**46** 45, 60
47 18, 36, etc.　　**48** 24, 48, etc.　　**49** 28, 56, etc.
50 30, 60, etc.　　**51** 1, 2, 11, 22　　**52** 1, 2, 4, 7, 14, 28
53 1, 2, 3, 5, 6, 10, 15, 30　　**54** 1, 2, 3, 4, 6, 9, 12, 18, 36
55 1, 3, 9, 27　　　　**56** 1, 2, 3, 6, 7, 14, 21, 42
57 1, 2, 4, 5, 8, 10, 20, 40　　**58** 1, 3, 5, 7, 15, 21, 35, 105
59 16　　　　**60** 49　　　　**61** 100
62 64　　　　**63** 61, 68, 75, 82　　**64** 0.9, 1.1, 1.3, 1.5
65 –14, –17, –20, –23　　**66** 63, 54, 45, 36　　**67** 75, 90, 105, 120
68 –2, 0, 2, 4　　　**69** 48, 40, 32, 24　　**70** 450, 500, 550, 600

Page 131
A

1 $\frac{2}{4}$　　**2** $\frac{2}{8}$　　**3** $\frac{3}{6}$　　**4** $\frac{5}{10}$　　**5** $\frac{4}{10}$

6 $\frac{4}{6}$　　**7** $\frac{6}{8}$　　**8** $\frac{8}{10}$　　**9** $\frac{1}{2}, \frac{5}{8}, \frac{3}{4}$　　**10** $\frac{3}{10}, \frac{2}{5}, \frac{1}{2}$

11 $3\frac{1}{2}$　　**12** $2\frac{1}{4}$　　**13** $3\frac{2}{3}$　　**14** $1\frac{3}{5}$　　**15** $2\frac{3}{8}$

16 $4\frac{1}{6}$　　**17** $3\frac{7}{10}$　　**18** $2\frac{49}{100}$　　**19** $\frac{8}{3}$　　**20** $\frac{19}{4}$

21 $\frac{71}{10}$　　**22** $\frac{23}{6}$　　**23** $\frac{43}{8}$　　**24** $\frac{137}{100}$　　**25** $\frac{32}{5}$

26 $\frac{43}{9}$　　**27** $\frac{9}{10}$　　**28** 6　　**29** $\frac{7}{100}$　　**30** $\frac{5}{10}$

31 5　　**32** $\frac{1}{10}$　　**33** $\frac{6}{100}$　　**34** $\frac{7}{10}$　　**35** (a) 0.2

(b) 0.5　　(c) 0.75　　(d) 0.93　　(e) 0.99　　(f) 1.07
36 2.47, 2.7, 4.27, 4.72　　**37** 1.59, 1.9, 5.19, 5.91
38 3.68, 3.8, 6.38, 6.8　　**39** 5.3, 5.37, 5.7, 5.73
40 3 m　　**41** 3 m　　**42** 7 m　　**43** 5 m　　**44** 10 m
45 £12　　**46** £6　　**47** £30　　**48** £87　　**49** £5

50 (a) $\frac{1}{2}$　　(b) 0.5　　(c) 50%

51 (a) $\frac{3}{4}$　　(b) 0.75　　(c) 75%

52 (a) $\frac{7}{10}$　　(b) 0.7　　(c) 70%

53 (a) $\frac{37}{100}$　　(b) 0.37　　(c) 37%

54 (a) $\frac{2}{5}$　　(b) 0.4　　(c) 40%

55 (a) $\frac{83}{100}$　　(b) 0.83　　(c) 83%

56 50　　**57** 150　　**58** 24　　**59** 12　　**60** 5 cm
61 90 cm　　**62** 21p　　**63** 48p　　**64** 7　　**65** 9
66 16　　**67** £1.50　　**68** 45p　　**69** £1.20　　**70** £2.75

Page 132
A

1 730　　**2** 93　　**3** 6.3 + 0.7　　**4** 38 + 62
5 747 + 500　　**6** 77 + 49　　**7** 7.3　　**8** 56
9 600 – 86　　**10** 8.4 – 0.4　　**11** 810 – 340　　**12** 272 – 57
13 713　　**14** 891　　**15** 1135　　**16** 1372
17 644　　**18** 173　　**19** 456　　**20** 233
21 1800　　**22** 4011　　**23** £4.88　　**24** £6.86
25 1565　　**26** 1483　　**27** £2.44　　**28** 20.6
29 294　　**30** 192　　**31** 0.7 × 4　　**32** 12 × 0
33 9 × 6　　**34** 0.6 × 3　　**35** 60　　**36** 9
37 48 ÷ 8　　**38** 150 ÷ 5　　**39** 20 ÷ 5　　**40** 31 ÷ 10
41 768　　**42** 2286　　**43** 4296　　**44** 2583
45 16 r 2　　**46** 28 r 4　　**47** 14 r 5　　**48** 34 r 6
49 816　　**50** 2700　　**51** 16.2　　**52** 25.2
53 43.5　　**54** 41.4　　**55** 22.4　　**56** 30.0
57 $5\frac{5}{7}$　　**58** $26\frac{3}{10}$　　**59** $7\frac{4}{9}$　　**60** $6\frac{3}{8}$
62 $22\frac{1}{4}$　　**62** $12\frac{5}{6}$　　**63** 42.5　　**64** 31.9

65 £1.80　　**66** £1.60　　**67** £1.95　　**68** £0.54
69 3600　　**70** 21　　**71** 115　　**72** 215

Page 133

1 4300 m　　**2** 5.87 km　　**3** 1.94 m　　**4** 260 cm
5 5 mm　　**6** 7.9 cm　　**7** 382 cm　　**8** 7.8 km
9 6250 g　　**10** 2300g　　**11** 3.74 kg　　**12** 0.5 kg
13 1400 ml　　**14** 3860 ml　　**15** 2.9 l　　**16** 0.48 l
17 (a) 2.3 cm　(b) 2.7 cm　　**18** (c) 35 mm　(d) 55 mm
19 (e) 150g　(f) 300g　　**20** (g) 0.7 l　(h) 1.6 l
21 800 ml　　**22** 1.72 m　　**23** 4.5kg　　**24** 20
25 6 cm²　　**26** 10 cm　　**27** (a) 24 cm², 20 cm
(b) 49 cm², 28 cm　　**28** 10 000 m²　　**29** 3 years
30 104 weeks　**31** 6 weeks　　**32** 72 hours　　**33** 390 mins.
34 5 mins.　　**35** 400 years　　**36** 150 mins.　　**37** Tuesday
38 Saturday　**39** Sunday　　**40** Thursday

41

12-HOUR CLOCK	24-HOUR CLOCK
4:25 pm	16:25
10:30 am	10:30
7:15 pm	19:15
8:42 am	08:42
9:06 pm	21:06
2:55 am	02:55
11:37 am	11:37
5:21 pm	17:21
7:49 am	07:49
11:11 pm	23:11

Page 134

1 quadrilateral　　　　**2** regular pentagon
3 scalene triangle　　　**4** irregular hexagon
5 isosceles triangle　　**6** quadrilateral
7 regular octagon　　　**8** irregular pentagon
9 (a) 4, 6, 8　　(b) 1, 4, 7　　(c) 2, 7
14 tetrahedron　　**15** cylinder　　**16** pentagonal prism
17 cuboid　　**18** octahedron　　**19** triangular prism
20 cone　　**21** square-based pyramid
22 14　　**23** 13　　**25** acute　　**26** obtuse　　**27** obtuse
28 acute　　**29** 105°　　**30** 31°　　**31** 127°　　**32** 69°
33 54°　　**34** 96°　　**35** 23°　　**36** 138°

Page 135
1 (a) 21°C　(b) 17°C　(c) Tuesday to Wednesday　(d) 14°C
3 (a) 5　(b) 16　(c) 6　(d) 26　(e) 1　(f) 60
4 (a) 40　(b) 6 hours　(c) 3　(d) 40　(e) 70　(f) 220

Page 136
A

1 4 and 9　**2** 8 and 11　**3** 7 and 8　**4** 6 and 6　**5** 3 and 9
6 9 and 20　**7** 3 and 14　**8** 5 and 20　**9** 6 and 9　**10** 3 and 15

B

1 29　　**2** 64　　**3** 43　　**4** 550　　**5** 56
6 17　　**7** 99　　**8** 81

C

1 (a) 11, 12　　(b) 13, 14　　(c) 29, 30　　(d) 21, 22
(e) 16, 17　　(f) 32, 33　　(g) 18, 19　　(h) 36, 37
(i) 39, 40　　**2** (a) 5, 13　　(b) 3, 23　　(c) 5, 17
(d) 7, 17　　(e) 13, 41　　(f) 11, 43　　(g) 3, 37
(h) 7, 31　　(i) 29, 61

3　326　　**4**　245　　**5**　427　　**6**　239
　– 174　　　　– 169　　　　× 3　　　　× 6
　152　　　　　76　　　　1281　　　　1434